Unusual Aquarium Fishes

Also by Alan Mark Fletcher

THE LAND AND PEOPLE OF THE GUIANAS

UNUSUAL AQUARIUM FISHES

Alan Mark Fletcher

J. B. Lippincott Company
PHILADELPHIA   NEW YORK

ISBN-0-397-31049-8

Library of Congress Catalog Card Number 68-10775
Fifth Printing
Typography by Tere LoPrete

For the photographs on the following pages the author gratefully credits:

New York Zoological Society: 47, 63, 105

A. van den Nieuwenhuizen: 26, 30, 31, 34, 35, 37, 39, 42, 44, 52, 53, 68, 75, 79, 80, 84, 85, 86, 89, 91, 94, 98, 102, 107, 110, 111, 114, 116, 118, 123, 126, 128, 131

Gene Wolfsheimer: 18, 19, 22, 23, 40, 48, 50, 55, 57, 59, 60, 81, 92, 96, 101, 113, 120, 121, 125

The photographs on pages 28, 61, 73, and 76 were taken by the author

The drawings on pages 16 and 64 are by Kay Reinhardt

A WORD OF APPRECIATION

Photographing live fishes is a tedious, time-consuming occupation. To make natural-looking fish portraits requires thorough knowledge of the subjects, much photographic skill, and infinite patience. Many of the photographs by A. van den Nieuwenhuizen of Holland and Gene Wolfsheimer of California are truly works of art. However, most remarkable is the fact that several of the photographs in this book show the fish subjects actually *doing* what makes them unusual. The series of photographs of *Copeina arnoldi* spawning and the photograph of kissing gouramis kissing, for example, can be fully appreciated only by someone who has attempted fish photography. The author is indeed fortunate to have received the cooperation of these two men who, in his opinion, are the greatest fish photographers in the world.

This book is dedicated to the author's daughters . . . Anne, Carol, Cynthia, and Lois . . . who, it is hoped, will grow up to have a deep appreciation not only of fishes but of all other life as well.

Preface

THE aquarium hobby is one of the largest in the world. Wherever there is enough leisure time to enjoy hobbies of any kind there will be people keeping fishes as pets. Even primitive peoples sometimes keep fishes in small pools or in old dugout canoes filled with water. It is estimated that in the United States alone as many as 20 million people keep fishes in aquariums! Nearly every school in the country has at least one aquarium, and cities around the world support beautiful public aquariums.

With all this familiarity with fishes, it seems rather surprising that so many aquarists have such limited knowledge of their pets. They know little more than how to feed them. But many of the fishes commonly kept in aquariums are more than beautiful. They have habits and characteristics so bizarre as to defy credibility.

Therefore, this book has two aims: to tell aquarists some of the unusual facts about their pets, and to inspire others to take up a fascinating hobby. Most of the fishes in this book are available as pets at least occasionally. Some of them are very common. The rest can be seen at any public aquarium. But more complete and detailed information should be sought before starting an aquarium.

Many more fishes with unusual characteristics or habits could have been included in this book. In the world of fishes, the unusual becomes usual. In fact, nearly every fish has *something* unusual about it. The fishes included seem to be the ones most appropriate to readers whose main interest is aquarium fishes.

In general, the fishes in this book are organized according to the pattern used by ichthyologists: the most primitive fishes first, the most highly developed fishes last. Closely related fishes are adjacent to each other.

It is the author's hope that through this book, devoted to the unusual aspects of fish life, others may discover what he considers to be the most fascinating and relaxing hobby of all.

Contents

A Note About the Words Fish and Fishes

THE singular of *fish* is *fish*. Dead fish in the market is always *fish*, whether speaking of one or many. However, few people know the correct plurals for live fishes. When speaking of more than one fish *of the same kind*, the plural is *fish*. When speaking of several fishes of *more than one kind* (species), the plural is *fishes*. Therefore, ten guppies are ten *fish*. Five guppies and five goldfish are ten *fishes*. Since a common guppy, a veiltail guppy, and a swordtail guppy are merely varieties of one *kind* (one species), collectively they would be three *fish*. The author has tried in this book to be correct and consistent about the usage of these plurals. Where *fishes* is used, the reader may assume that more than one species is being referred to.

Unusual Aquarium Fishes

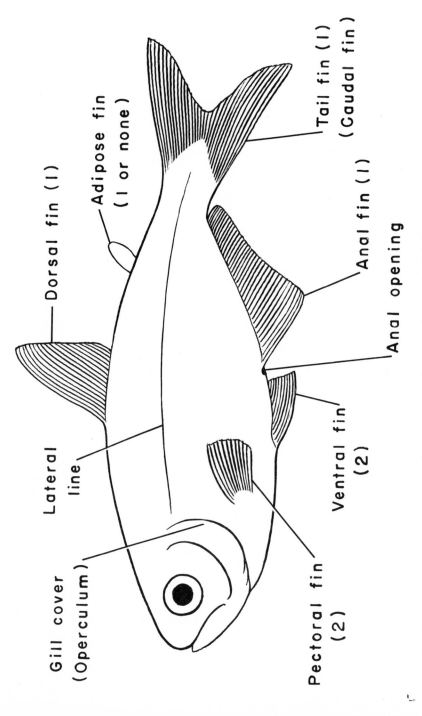

Dorsal fin (1)

Adipose fin
(1 or none)

Tail fin (1)
(Caudal fin)

Anal fin (1)

Anal opening

Lateral
line

Ventral fin
(2)

Gill cover
(Operculum)

Pectoral fin
(2)

Some external parts of a typical fish.

1 »• *The Blind Cave Tetra*

LIVING in underground caves in several parts of the world are fishes that have been isolated in total darkness for so long that they no longer have the ability to see at all. In fact, some have even lost their eyes. Where the eye once was, there now is just a circular outline. Somehow, the blindness has become inherited. Blind cave fishes kept in well-lighted aquariums continue to produce blind offspring generation after generation. Best known to aquarists is the blind cave tetra, *Anoptichthys jordani,* first found in a Mexican cave in 1935.

Aquarists acquiring the blind cave tetra tend to feel sorry for it at first, but pity soon turns to admiration as the fish is observed. It gets along very well indeed, even in the company of fishes with very good eyes.

The blind cave tetra is an attractive, delicately shaped fish that grows to only three inches. It is plain pink all over, having lost its pigments along with its eyes. Scientists believe that the blind cave tetra developed from another Mexican fish, *Astyanax mexicanus,* which is very common in streams in the vicinity of the blind tetra's subterranean home. It appears likely that at some time in ages past, specimens of *Astyanax* swam into the

The blind cave tetra lives in a cave in Mexico. Note that the area where the eyes should be is merely covered with skin.

cave and could not find their way out again. Eventually they lost both their eyes and their coloring.

How cave-adapted animals like the blind cave tetra could have come into being is a question that fascinates scientists, some of whom have given a lot of thought and study to the origin of these creatures. Blind cave fishes are not unique. Salamanders, crayfish, spiders, centipedes and other animals live in caves. Many of them have lost their coloring and their eyes just as the blind cave tetra has. Scientists conclude that there must be some reason for cave animals of many kinds to lose both eyes and coloring, and the reason is believed to be what has been called "metabolic economy." Food is scarce in caves, and it takes food to grow eyes and coloring. While eyesight and colors are important to animals in the sunlit world, neither has any value in a totally dark cave. Over many centuries of time, any unneeded

ASTYANAX MEXICANUS, *a common small fish of Mexico, is believed to be the fish from which the blind cave tetra developed.*

features would naturally tend to disappear as a way of making the best possible use of the limited food supply. Conversely, features important to cave life would tend to become more pronounced.

Blind cave tetras are a real phenomenon in captivity. Placed in an aquarium they quickly take the measure of their surroundings. With little difficulty they learn not only the dimensions of the aquarium, but also where such obstacles as rocks and plants are located. They rarely bump into anything. Furthermore, they have no difficulty locating their food. Even small swimming creatures are readily caught and eaten by the blind cave tetra.

In this fish's breeding habits we have a clue to how it gets along so well despite its apparent handicap. Blind cave tetras in an aquarium are reported to lay their eggs among fine-leaf plants. (No one knows how they spawn in their native cave, since plants cannot grow in the dark.) First the female scatters her eggs, which stick to the plants. Then the male moves in and, sometimes without any contact with the female, he fertilizes the eggs. Here is the clue: How does the male know exactly where the eggs are? He can't see them. He must *smell* them. It seems likely that the blind cave tetra has an unusually keen sense of smell that serves the fish nearly as well as the eyes serve normal fishes. Of course, there may be other well-developed senses as well.

The eggs of the blind cave tetra hatch in two days or less, depending upon the temperature. If the fry are placed under a low-power microscope they are seen to have primitive black-pigmented eyes. By the seventh day, skin has grown over the eyes completely. It is not known whether or not the young fish can see in those first days of life.

The blind cave tetra is a perfect example of how an animal (or a person, for that matter) can live a successful life in spite of a severe handicap.

2 »• *Hatchet Fishes*

MOST people know something of the flying fishes that inhabit the warm waters of the Atlantic and Pacific Oceans. Their ability to glide through the air is so well developed that their flights occasionally carry them onto the decks of ships. Few people, however, know about the lovely little freshwater flying fishes, better known as hatchet fishes. Many aquarists who keep these popular fishes in aquariums have never heard of their flying ability, which is really quite remarkable for their small size (one to four inches).

For their size, hatchet fishes fly at least as well as the better-known marine flying fishes. Hatchets can propel themselves through the air for fifteen feet and more, while the flights of marine flying fishes, which are many times larger, rarely exceed two hundred feet. Furthermore, it has been proven that hatchets actually propel themselves through the air by flapping their pectoral fins (their "wings"). Marine flying fishes use their fins only for gliding.

What advantage is flight to a fish? Observing hatchet fishes in nature, the answer is readily apparent: it is a means of escaping from enemies. Hatchets swim in groups just under the surface of the water, where they are continually searching for insects and small aquatic animals. When a larger fish approaches to eat them, the hatchets are in the air and far away from danger in an instant.

Hatchet fishes get their name from their peculiar shape. From the side, they look like deep triangles, rounded only at the bottom, not unlike the shape of a hatchet. From the front, they are thinner than a cracker, tapering to a knife edge along the belly. It is pretty well established that the proportionately deep body contains large muscles that contribute to the fish's ability to flap its fins in flight.

Hatchet fishes are so named because their bodies are shaped somewhat like the head of a hatchet.

One species or more of hatchet fish is found over most of the South American continent north of Buenos Aires, Argentina. That is not to imply that every stream and lake has them, but they are very widely distributed.

Even though they are not among the most hardy fishes, hatchet fishes are very popular with aquarists. Their unusual shape and their bright silvery appearance make them a nice contrast to other more conventional fishes. It should go without saying that any aquarium containing hatchet fishes should be covered with a piece of glass; otherwise they surely will be found on the floor one day, dried to a crisp.

Martha's hatchet fish is a graceful little creature. All of the hatchet fishes are capable of flying through the air for surprising distances.

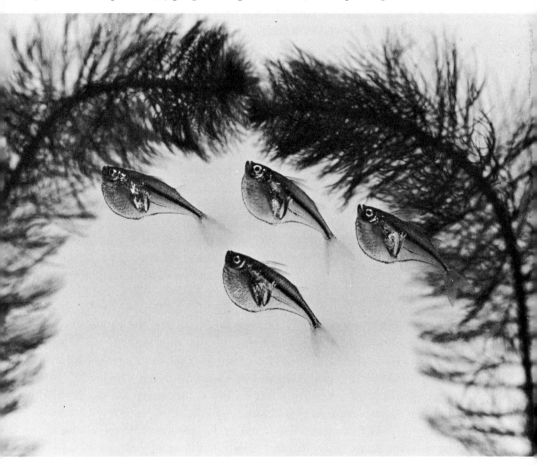

3 »• *The Piranha*

To the outside world the piranha typifies sudden, painful death in the Amazon jungle. Nearly every tropical-fish store has had, at one time or another, an aquarium containing piranhas on display, with a cardboard skeleton draped over a side, a plastic skull on the gravel, and a sign lettered "THE MAN-EATING FISH FROM THE AMAZON."

That the piranha, piraña, caribe, or pirai (depending upon the country in which the fish is found) is fully equipped to be a most dangerous creature there can be no doubt. Whether or not these fishes are really so dangerous as their reputation indicates is widely debated, one's opinion being based largely on the kind of experience he has had with them.

The truth of it is that in some places the piranha is extremely dangerous, and in others it is quite harmless most of the time. In many waters of the upper Amazon, Indian children swim and play in water that teems with the fish. Yet in Guyana's Abary River one doesn't dare place his hands in the water. The author has caught piranhas (the same kind as in the Abary) and then had himself photographed sitting in the water holding a live piranha in the exact spot where the fish had just been caught!

There seems to be good evidence that even where the piranha is usually harmless, under certain conditions it can be provoked or stimulated into attacking. It is said that an injury large enough to cause substantial bleeding is likely to draw piranhas from some distance and stimulate them to make a frenzied attack. Indians who sustain a cut while in the water are known to get out of the water as quickly as they can.

Many wild tales have been told about piranhas. Most of them have some basis in truth, and reflect some exaggeration as well.

For instance, it has been reported that in some parts of South America ranchers desiring to drive cattle across a piranha-infested river use a decoy. They supposedly drag an unfortunate cow into the river some distance above the place where the drive is to take place. Then, when the piranhas are thoroughly occupied with eating the decoy, the ranchers quickly drive the rest of the cattle across the river. Perhaps this technique *has* been used at times, but it seems doubtful that ranchers would be willing to lose even one cow if they could avoid it.

Some years ago an Italian motion picture company produced a movie of South America in which a caiman (South American alligator) was eaten by piranhas. In vivid technicolor the camera ground away as the caiman was devoured by dozens of piranhas, the water being turned into a pink froth while the voracious fish reduced the great reptile to a skeleton. The movie camera in this instance could not have lied.

There can be no doubt that piranhas, wherever they are found, at least occasionally eat animals that wander into the water. But two facts prove that piranhas do not depend upon these animals for food. In the first place, all sorts of animals, as well as humans, wander in and out of piranha waters with little concern. If this were very hazardous, they would have learned long ago that they should stay out of the water. In the second place, where piranhas occur, they are usually abundant. The occasional animal that wanders into the water would never be sufficient to support a large population of these fish; so piranhas eat other fishes. It can also be assumed that piranhas at least occasionally eat each other. Of dozens of mature piranhas caught by the author, not one ever had perfect fins. All of them bore evidence of being nipped at by their kin.

There are about sixteen species of piranha. While the most dangerous of the species have large, very sharp teeth, the upper and lower set of which fit perfectly together, these remarkable fishes have other characteristics that enhance their biting ability.

These two large black piranhas (about twelve inches in length) give no hint of their vicious nature because their sharp teeth are hidden.

Their lower jaws are sturdy, and they swing shut at an angle that gives maximum leverage. Their deep flat bodies, which offer resistance when swung sideways through the water, add to the leverage. Incredibly large muscles are attached to the jaws. The muscles are so sturdy that when you look down the throat of a large specimen, there seems scarcely to be enough room for swallowing. When the fish clamps down on a victim, it grabs firmly and twists its body violently, until a piece is torn loose. In a word, the piranha is a most efficient biting machine. Every part of its body seems to make a contribution to this function.

A personal experience illustrates the power of the piranha's jaws very well. Fishing for piranhas in Guyana's upper Abary

River, the author was using special heavy-shanked steel fish-hooks. Twice piranhas bit completely through the strong hooks (not the *line*, but the *hooks!*) as they were being lifted out of the water. Several others had broken teeth from their attempts to crunch through the hooks. A man with a pair of pliers would have had difficulty snipping through those hooks!

Piranhas are generally thought of as very small fishes, but they grow larger than most people realize. Probably the average is around six inches. However, eighteen-inchers have been caught by the author, and they undoubtedly grow even larger.

Piranhas have a very wide distribution in South America. They are found in rivers, streams, and lakes throughout the northern two-thirds of the continent east of the Andes Mountains. This would include most of Brazil and Peru, and all of the countries to the north of them. In rivers and streams they are most likely to be found in the deeper water, where it flows with a slow, steady current.

These ferocious fishes adapt readily to aquarium conditions. Until a federal law was passed forbidding the importation of piranhas, they were frequently seen in private collections and on display in pet stores. Many curious people have wandered into pet stores just to see the "terrible cannibal fish of the Amazon," and more than a few have left with an aquarium and a new hobby. Despite the law, a few piranhas still find their way into the aquariums of hobbyists, for the average customs inspector is totally incapable of distinguishing the piranha from a dozen other fishes that are commonly imported from South America.

Curiously, in an aquarium, piranhas often become quite shy. Except for an occasional glimpse of those horrible teeth, there is little to indicate their wild characteristics.

In captivity, piranhas are usually fed live fishes and worms. They prefer their food on the move. When a small fish is placed in the aquarium, the piranha looks it over with studied deliberation. Then, with a lightning-fast dash, the hapless fish is seized

A mounted head of a sixteen-inch black piranha caught by the author in the Abary River, Guyana.

from the rear and neatly clipped in two. The forward portion may be eaten next, or it may be left to die in a few minutes. So long as it keeps struggling, the piranha may take another bite. Once dead, the fish is usually ignored.

Surely in all the world there is no more efficient biting animal than the South American piranha. Even the much-feared sharks cannot compare with the piranha.

4 »• *Copeina Arnoldi*

EVERYONE knows that fishes lay their eggs in water, but in the unusual world of fishes one might expect to find an exception. *Copeina arnoldi,* a pretty little fish from northern South America, is that exception.

All fishes have some means of protecting their eggs and often their young as well from the unfriendly world into which they are brought. Some build nests, which they guard with their lives. Some bury their eggs in the bottom of the lake or stream. Others carry them about attached to one of the parents in some way. Still others merely depend on laying such huge quantities of eggs that some are sure to survive. *Copeina* lays its eggs above the water, away from the hungry mouths of other fishes.

In the small jungle streams that are home to *Copeina,* there are always plenty of leaves, sticks, and rocks overhanging the water. At spawning time, the male searches out a leaf, limb, or rock that hangs within two inches of the water. Then he coaxes an egg-laden female underneath. For a few minutes they swim about in great excitement. Finally the two assume a side-by-side position, and with fins clasped together they jump out of the water onto the overhanging object, where they remain (apparently by suction of their fins) for several seconds, while the female lays several eggs. The male fertilizes them immediately, and then the parents fall back into the water. The spawning act is repeated over and over again, until about a hundred eggs have been stuck to the surface. All together the gelatinous mass of eggs covers an area of about two square inches.

At this point the female's work is completed, but the male's work has only begun. Eggs laid above the water would quickly dry out, thereby killing the embryos; thus for the three days it takes the eggs to mature and hatch, the male *Copeina* periodically splashes water over them to keep them moist. Interestingly, the father apparently knows that if he stayed immediately under

CopEINA ARNOLDI *is widely known for its strange breeding habits. In the photograph below, a pair is resting just under the surface of the water. Then they swim rapidly through the surface (photograph two) and jump onto an overhanging leaf, as in the third photograph. The fourth one shows the female falling back into the water as the male still clings to the leaf. After the eggs are deposited on the leaf and are fertilized by the male, he remains under the leaf (photograph five) and with his tail splashes water on the eggs to keep them from drying out.*

I

2   3

4   5

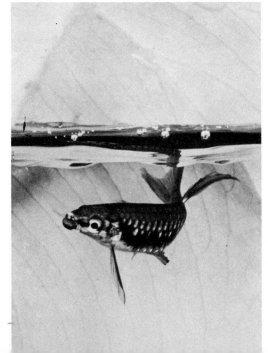

the eggs he would attract attention to them. He remains some distance away, coming under the eggs only when he wants to splash them with water. When the babies hatch, they fall into the water, and they set out on their own, for they receive no further assistance from the parent.

Copeina arnoldi are easily maintained in aquariums, and with a wholesome diet it is not difficult to induce them to spawn in captivity. Aquarists generally place a piece of slate or opaque glass at an angle close to the surface of the water. The parents readily accept such surfaces for their brood.

One cannot help wondering how a fish could develop such a unique method of protecting its offspring. *Copeina arnoldi* appears to be the only fish with this particular "gimmick." Even its closest fish relative, *Copeina guttata,* gives not the slightest hint of its cousin's habits, for *Copeina guttata* merely lays its eggs in a depression in the sand at the bottom of the stream.

5 »• *The Electric Eel*

WHAT quirk of nature could create a fish with the ability to generate electricity?

Two native fish collectors were dragging a long two-man seine through the murky waters of a South American river. All of a sudden, one of the fishermen ran out of the water screaming like a man on fire. He had brushed against an electric eel and had received a painful shock. Only after a lot of loud scolding from his boss would the Indian return to the water. Such experiences with one of the most unbelievable fishes in the world are common.

Some public aquariums have displays in which large electric eels are put through their paces. Wearing arm-long heavy rubber gloves, an attendant lifts the eel from its tank and touches its sides against metal contacts connected to a whole battery of electric lights. The lights glow as brilliantly as if they had been connected to a regular electric current.

The unusual electrical properties of the electric eel have long interested scientists. During World War II, the United States Government began sponsoring research on the electric eel. From the beginning of these experiments, the eels have been supplied by Paramount Aquarium, Inc., whose planes regularly bring back loads of tropical fishes from South America. The eels are placed in specially-made wooden troughs lined with heavy plastic. You may be certain that the crew of the aircraft stay some distance from those impressive creatures!

Electric eels are rather ugly, sluggish creatures. They need no beauty, because they have no friends. They need not be active, because they have no enemies. Every living thing in the water avoids the electric eel.

Although they may grow to more than eight feet, the average size is closer to three or four feet. The body is brown, scaleless, and very slippery. All of the vital organs of the electric eel are in the front fifth of the body. The rest of the body is muscle and electric organs. Electric eels are nearly blind.

Scientists who have studied these eels report that a mature specimen can produce as much as 600 volts and 1000 watts of electricity for a brief instant. This amount of voltage is enough, brief though it is, to stun nearly any living thing that brushes against it. The electric eel uses its electrical power to defend itself when it must, but usually the current is used to stun fishes and other animals so the eel can catch and eat them.

There are several sets of electrical organs in the eel's body. All of them are modified muscles; that is, they are muscles that have become adapted to produce electricity. The individual sets are used separately so that the fish can sustain its shocking power over a longer time. One set of organs also sends out impulses that help the electric eel locate its prospective food. When sent out

Among several fishes capable of generating electricity, the electric eel is the champion. Large ones have been known to produce an electric force of 600 volts.

into the water, the impulses bounce off objects in front and travel back to receiving glands in the fish's head, much like radar. Thus the eel is guided to its prey without the use of its weak eyes, which frequently would be useless anyway, because electric eels often live in very muddy water.

One important oddity of the electric eel completely baffles scientists. Have you ever scuffed your shoes across a rug to build up an electrical charge so that you could shock someone else? If you have, you know that *both* of you feel the shock. So it must be with the eel when it shocks a victim, but no one knows how the eel manages to go unharmed, while the victim is knocked unconscious.

Electric eels must go to the surface to gulp mouthfuls of air. Although it has gills like other fishes, the eel soon dies if it is prevented from coming to the surface, because it has become so dependent upon breathing atmospheric air.

Other fishes also produce electricity, but none approaches the great ability of the electric eel. The second best-known electric fish is the electric catfish of Africa, which is a pretty potent shocker in its own right.

The electric catfish of Africa can produce enough electricity to deliver a painful shock, but it is not as potent as the electric eel.

While much has been learned about the electricity-producing ability of the various electric fishes, little is as yet known about exactly *how* the electricity is produced. Research with the electric eel may one day reveal important information about humans, because it is known that all nerves send their messages in part by means of electrical impulses.

Electric eels and other "shocking" fishes are hardly pets for the home aquarium, but most public aquariums have them on display.

6 »• *The "Plastic" Goldfish*

IT is estimated that more than 75 million goldfish are reared and sold each year in the United States alone. While this is a very large figure, when nearly every ten-cent store and variety store in the country has a huge tank filled with hundreds of goldfish, the figure is not so difficult to believe. Obviously the fish must be selling or the stores would not stock them. For each goldfish sold, a dollar or two in aquariums, equipment, and food is spent in addition to the purchase price of the fish. The goldfish is big business in the United States. However, the person who keeps a fish or two in a globe has no idea that his pets are among the most unusual of fishes.

The goldfish may well be the most plastic animal in the world. That is, it is capable of almost limitless variation in form and color. Through many centuries of time, varieties of goldfish have been developed that bear practically no resemblance to the wild form, and little resemblance to each other.

Carassius auratus, the wild goldfish, is native to the temperate regions of Asia. The wild fish is olive-colored, rather than golden. Records of goldfish in cultivation go back about fifteen hundred years, but it seems likely that men have been keeping them in

A commercial type of goldfish of the variety commonly sold in pet stores. This fish has a slightly longer tail fin than the "common" goldfish.

pools and tanks for much longer. Most of the varieties of goldfish were developed by the Koreans, Chinese, and Japanese, in that order. The first specimens are believed to have been brought to America from Asia in 1874 by one Admiral Ammon. At that time they were already beautifully developed.

Asian peoples are known for their patience, an attribute of great importance in the development of the goldfish. Westerners would probably never have had the patience to select and breed these fish for special characteristics over hundreds of years, but to the Asians this was a fascinating challenge. Fancy goldfish are a living tribute to the insight, intelligence, and skill of countless unknown people who had no knowledge of modern genetics.

There are more kinds of goldfish than could be described here (whole books have been written on the subject), but some of the more important goldfish varieties follow. They indicate the tremendous variation of which the goldfish is capable.

Comet. A goldfish with a long narrow body and flowing fins. The tail fin may be as long as the body. Color is usually red or golden.

Shubunkin. A narrow-bodied goldfish with somewhat elongated fins. The main feature of this variety is its combination of colors, which may include red, white, black, and blue. The best specimens have a lot of blue.

Japanese fringetail. A truly elegant fish with a short, chunky body. In the best specimens the body is as deep as it is long. All of the fins are greatly elongated, but its flowing *double* tail may be more than twice the length of the body. Usually red or red and white.

Japanese nymph. A short, deep-bodied goldfish with a very large dorsal fin and a long, deeply notched single tail. Usually reddish or golden.

Veiltail telescope. The body and fins are similar to the Japanese fringetail, but this fish has huge, froglike eyes. Color may be red, olive, brown, white, or calico (combinations of several colors).

Black moor telescope. Similar to the veiltail telescope, but the body and fins are solid velvety black. A magnificent fish at its best.

Celestial. This variety has huge bulbous eyes that point skyward.

Lionhead. A chunky, deep-bodied goldfish with a short double tail, no dorsal fin, and a large raspberrylike growth over the head and gill covers. Usually golden or white. The "raspberry" is red, regardless of the body color.

Oranda. A veiltail or fringetail goldfish with the lionhead's "raspberry."

A veiltail goldfish. Notice the long, flowing fins and the chunky body.

While there are many more varieties of goldfish, these are sufficient to illustrate the tremendous range of forms. It is difficult to believe that a shubunkin is really the same fish as a lionhead. Yet, if the two varieties are put together under the right circumstances, they will interbreed as if they were totally unaware of the great difference.

Goldfish are spring spawners. In fact, they need several months of cool weather to come into breeding condition. Goldfish kept continually in warm water will never breed. In a cool aquarium, goldfish begin to spawn in February or March. Outdoors they spawn several weeks later.

There is only one reliable way to determine the sex of goldfish. Several weeks before spawning, the males develop whitish bumps (tubercles) on their gill covers. During the same time the males chase the females incessantly. Thousands of tiny eggs are scattered among fine-leaf plants near the surface. The parents give no care to the eggs or young. Once spawning is completed, they will eat all the eggs they can find.

Rearing baby goldfish is relatively easy, but to produce high quality specimens requires great care and much experience. Even the offspring of champion parents grow into ordinary fish unless they are reared skillfully. They must have just the right amount of space at just the right time, because they become stunted if they are crowded, and they grow thin if they have too much space. They must be fed nutritious foods (such as chopped earthworms and Pablum) many times a day. Curiously, very few baby goldfish ever grow into quality fish, even with the best

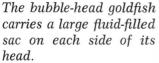

The bubble-head goldfish carries a large fluid-filled sac on each side of its head.

care. Out of a spawning of a thousand eggs from prize parents, only a dozen young may turn out to be close to the quality of the parents. An experienced goldfish breeder is constantly culling out inferior babies as they become apparent.

The so-called common goldfish is a remarkable creature.

7 »• *The European Bitterling*

SOME fishes are noted for the clever ways in which they protect their young. One of the most puzzling aspects of this protective behavior is that it is somehow inherited. Fishes cannot talk with each other, yet each generation carries out exactly the same breeding procedures as its parents did, and as all preceding generations did as well. When breeding time comes, the prospective parents automatically go about the business of preparing for and caring for their young. Perhaps someday we will know for sure just how fishes transmit behavior patterns to their young, but for the present we can only assume that behavior is inherited with the genes of the egg and sperm cells, along with the physical characteristics.

Through countless centuries the bitterling of Central Europe has worked out a truly ingenious reproductive pattern. As spawning time approaches, the female bitterling develops an inch-long tube from her abdomen, called an ovipositor. After being coaxed by the male, the female carefully places the end of her ovipositor between the open halves of a living freshwater clam's shell. A few eggs are deposited. The male then sprays his sperms over the clam, and as clams are constantly drawing in water, the sperms are drawn in with the water to fertilize the eggs. Both fish may move on to another clam, where a few more eggs are deposited and fertilized. The pair may continue to produce for several days. It is a mystery why the clam tolerates this intrusion, because at the slightest disturbance a clam will normally close its shell with a snap. So far as is known, the female bitterling's ovipositor is never caught in the clam's shell.

Even after the eggs hatch, the baby bitterlings remain inside the clam for several days, and then they swim out to face the world.

Except for its silvery coloring, the three-inch bitterling looks much like its cousin, the common goldfish. The bitterling has several close relatives in Asia with similar unique breeding habits.

Bitterlings make interesting aquarium pets, if the water is kept cool (not above 80 degrees). With plenty of good food, it is possible to induce them to demonstrate their breeding skill. Of course, the aquarium must also have several live freshwater clams.

There is nothing unusual about the appearance of the European bitterling, but the females of this species deposit their eggs for safe-keeping inside living freshwater clams.

8 »• *The Upside-down Catfish*

A FISH that swims upside down! Many people cannot tell whether a fish is right side up or upside down, but to those who know fishes at all, this is truly a remarkable behavior characteristic. When this little catfish swims or when it is resting, its dorsal fin is usually on the bottom. Dorsal fins are always on the back of a fish. There are a number of fishes that habitually swim with their heads up or down at a steep angle, but these are the only fishes that swim completely turned over.

Several members of the African catfish family Mochokidae are upside-down swimmers. The best known of these to American aquarists is *Synodontis nigriventris*, which comes from the Congo River. To most aquarists this is *the* upside-down catfish. *S. nigriventris* is a lovely fish, marbled all over, even on its fins and barbels, in dark brown and white. Aquarium specimens rarely exceed four inches, though scientists believe the fish may grow much larger in the wild.

Most catfishes have very sharp spines on their dorsal and ventral fins, which they use as a defense against being eaten by larger fishes and other animals. The upside-down catfish has an additional refinement, however. It can lock its spines in an upright position, so firmly that if they are pressed down they may actually break before they give way. When a larger fish or a water snake seizes a spined catfish, the spines are quickly erected. The predator receives a painful puncture in its mouth and promptly spits out its prey. Once the author found a water snake that had a large catfish caught in its throat. With the spines erected, the snake was unable to move the catfish in either direction. Both snake and catfish died as a result of this encounter.

Upside-down catfish are delightful aquarium pets. They eat any foods offered to them, and they are generally peaceful.

Two upside-down catfish rest in a typical position on the underside of a rock.

When they swim around (usually in the evening) they are either upside down or right side up. Sometimes they revolve as they go through the water, as if they are unable to make up their minds which way they should swim. At rest they pick the underside of a leaf or a rock, to which they cling, upside down, of course.

9 »• *The Common Eel*

THE common eel is much disdained, for several reasons. In the first place, the eel looks more like a snake than a fish, and most people dislike snakes. Second, the eel, because of its tremendous appetite, is often a nuisance to fishermen. Third, it is one of the toughest and most durable fishes known. When caught, the eel lives for several hours. Fourth, the eel is one of the slimiest, slipperiest fish in the world, as any fisherman can testify. Nevertheless, the common eel has a fascinating life history, and makes an interesting aquarium pet.

Much mystery has surrounded the life story of the eel since the beginning of recorded history. People had always watched mature eels leaving their freshwater homes in the autumn to swim out to sea. In the spring baby eels were seen returning to fresh water in great numbers. It was assumed that these baby eels, or elvers, as they are called, were the young of those adults that entered the sea the preceding autumn. However, the story of the eel has turned out to be far more complicated and interesting than that. Through masterful scientific detective work by a number of people over many years, we are now able to fit together most of the pieces in the eel's amazing life cycle.

The first important piece of information came in the 1890's, when two Italian scientists made a great discovery. Thin willow-leaf-shaped fishes called *leptocephali* had been known for a long time to be plentiful in the northern half of the Atlantic Ocean, often occurring thousands of miles from shore. The Italian scientists collected some specimens that appeared to have some characteristics of both eels and *leptocephali*. Further study proved that *leptocephali* are really baby eels. What the scientists had collected were *leptocephali* that were in the process of changing to elvers. Thus was one of the eel's secrets revealed, but still, no one knew where or how eels reproduced.

The next important pieces of information were discovered by Johannes Schmidt, who for thirty years in the early part of the twentieth century studied eels under the sponsorship of the Government of Denmark. Dr. Schmidt secured the assistance of commercial ships sailing all over the Atlantic Ocean. Seamen of the ships collected *leptocephali* wherever they travelled over the ocean and recorded the location and date of each catch. Back in the laboratory Dr. Schmidt and his staff measured the *leptocephali* and made other studies of them. It turned out that the *leptocephali* were smaller and smaller the farther south they were collected. The smallest ones were collected in two overlapping areas east of the Bahama Islands. This had to be the eel's spawning grounds.

With the additional contributions of other scientists most of the eel's story is now known. There are two species of eels: *Anguilla bostoniensis* of North America, and *Anguilla anguilla* of Europe. Along the coasts of both continents baby eels enter the mouths of rivers and creeks, usually in the spring. The males stay in the brackish and salt water, but the females swim far upstream, sometimes even over land into lakes, where the water is completely fresh. The females may stay in their freshwater homes for as long as twenty years, and they may grow to more than five feet, but one autumn they head downstream toward the ocean, where they are joined by much younger and smaller males. For as much as a year they journey to the breeding area east of the Bahamas, where they spawn at a depth of 1500 feet and then die. The eggs float to the surface and hatch into *leptocephali*. The baby eels begin their long journey northward, a journey of as much as three years for the European eel and about one year for the American species. At first they all travel the same route, but eventually they begin to separate, the babies of American parents heading westward and the babies of European parents heading toward the northeast. Finally, all the babies that have survived the long journey reach the streams that their parents had entered many years before. Toward the end of the homeward journey, the *leptocephali* slowly change into elvers. By the time they reach the coast they have become perfect four-inch eels.

Young eels are easily kept in aquariums. They eat any food

A group of large common eels on display in a public aquarium.

offered to them, and they can endure a wide range of temperatures. Aquarium-reared eels are usually very light colored in comparison to their wild counterparts, which are dark olive. Some pet eels have become tame enough to eat food out of their owner's hand. A huge eel kept for many years at the public aquarium of the Pennsylvania Fish Commission's fish hatchery in Mt. Pleasant, Pa., is so aggressive that it will bite any hand placed in the water.

It is reported that eels in an aquarium will occasionally bury themselves in the gravel with only their heads sticking out.

Young eels can be a source of much fun for a home or school aquarium.

10 »• *The Halfbeak*

THE halfbeak is included in this book partly because of the amazing photograph of a female halfbeak giving birth to a baby.

A very rare photograph of a live-bearing fish (a halfbeak) giving birth.

Many of the well-known aquarium fishes, including the ever-popular guppy, give birth to living young rather than eggs, but photographs of the process are rare.

The halfbeak is a superb fighter, second in ability only to the fighting fish itself. The people of Thailand have for many years bred halfbeaks for fighting, until the present cultivated strain far outperforms its wild counterpart.

Fights are staged in this way: Two halfbeaks are placed in a shallow earthenware bowl, filled with a few inches of water. The fish eye each other for a moment and then close in for the attack. They may lock jaws and shake and roll over. Or one fish may clamp its large jaws over the other fish's head. Obviously, the fish that grabs the other has a temporary advantage. Such "wrestling" sometimes continues for hours, until one of the combatants becomes too exhausted to continue. The one that gives up is the loser, and the men who have placed their bets on this fish lose as well. Occasionally, both contestants become exhausted at the same time. When this happens, the winner is decided by a point system. That is, the fish administering the most holds during the fight scores the larger number of points and is declared the winner.

In Southeast Asia and the East Indies, where the halfbeak is native, it is a valuable eater of mosquito larvae. If the quiet streams, ditches, and ponds where the halfbeak lives were without this fish, the mosquito population would undoubtedly become unbearably large.

Halfbeaks make interesting aquarium pets, and they ordinarily do not fight with other kinds of fishes their own size. Very small fishes are likely to be eaten, however.

11 »• *Desert Pupfishes*

HIGH temperatures are fatal to fishes. Turning up the electric heater in the aquarium will kill an aquarium full of "tropical" fishes. By the time the temperature reaches 90 degrees, the fishes will show signs of distress. Before it reaches 100 degrees, they will all be dead. Lack of oxygen is the basic reason for the fatal effects of high temperatures. Warm water can hold much less dissolved oxygen than cold water. In effect, a fish in warm water suffocates. Also, beyond a temperature of about 120 degrees, the living quality of most animal tissues is destroyed.

The above notwithstanding, there are a few small fishes that seem to thrive in warm water. In many isolated places in the desert country of southern California, Arizona, and northern Mexico, there are warm-water springs. In some of these springs, small fish may be seen darting about. Temperatures in these

Desert pupfishes are known for their ability to live in springs so hot that the water is uncomfortable to the human touch.

springs have been found to be as high as 138 degrees! Just how do these fishes manage to stay alive in water nearly hot enough to cook an egg?

Studies have shown that the immediate surface layer of the water ranges from 85 degrees to 95 degrees. It is in this layer that the desert pupfishes live. They may swim into the warmer water for brief periods, but it is a certainty that they soon retreat to the cooler layer. An aquarist who had kept pupfishes in an aquarium reported in *The Aquarium* magazine that by accident the water temperature went up to 110 degrees. Two fish died and fifteen lived. The next day the temperature returned to 85 degrees, and the fifteen remaining fish showed no ill effects from their experience.

All of the desert pupfishes belong to the genus *Cyprinodon.* They are closely related to the killifishes that are common along the east coast and the gulf states. Pupfishes are never sold in stores, but aquarists who live near the natural habitat of these fishes sometimes collect them.

12 »• *Annual Fishes*

THERE is a group of extremely colorful small fishes from South America and Africa referred to as the annual fishes. They inhabit regions in which seasonal droughts dry up many of the ponds. The annual fishes live in these temporary ponds. When the ponds dry up all the fishes die. Hence, the reason for the name *annual* fishes. Through a remarkable life cycle a new generation is produced each year. In about six months' time the annual fishes are born, they grow to maturity, and they produce the seeds of the next generation before death by drying overtakes them.

Perhaps a half dozen species of annual fishes are available to aquarists at least occasionally, but by far the best known are the Argentine pearl fishes, *Cynolebias bellottii* and *Cynolebias nigripinnis;* these can be used as typical of the group. The male pearl fish at its best is navy blue with an indigo tint all over, including its fins. Over the body and fins are rows of white dots that contrast beautifully with the dark blue base coloring. When the male swims, it is reminiscent of a flag fluttering in the breeze. Except for general body shape, the female looks like a different species. Her fins are smaller, and she is an overall olive color, with brown bars on body and fins.

The spawning of a male and two female Argentine pearl fish. The male is just beginning to burrow into the soil on the bottom of the aquarium.

Writing in *The Aquarium* in 1940, a man who had observed the pearl fish in Argentina wrote: "The breeding habits of this fish are extremely interesting. When a male and female fish are ready for spawning, the male will swim back and forth around the female, meanwhile displaying the handsomest colors that could meet the eye. Then he will swim along with his mouth lowered, burrowing or digging up the bottom until he discovers what he thinks is a suitable place in which to place the eggs. He will then press his body against his mate, sometimes almost wrapping himself around the female, which has been following him. Now he will stand squarely on his head and with his nose bore a fairly deep hole in the ground. Then his mate will come swimming to him, pressing her body against his. Then in the midst of a trembling motion, while pressing their bodies against each other, an egg is discharged. This is immediately fertilized by the male. After a few seconds the egg is placed in the little hole in the ground prepared by the male fish. One or two quick motions and the egg is completely covered with dirt. These antics continue in this way for a few hours, perhaps all day long."

When the ponds dry up, the adult pearl fish perish, but their eggs remain alive in the mud. As the rains return, the eggs hatch, and the next generation begins its frantic life's pace—without ever having seen its parents.

Although the pearl fish has been known to aquarists for at least thirty years, it is only in recent years that they have learned

*A pair of African annual fish (*NOTHOBRANCHIUS GUENTHERI*) prepare to spawn in the same manner as the pearl fish. Note the way in which the male embraces the female with his dorsal fin.*

to breed it. For years, attempts to rear the pearl fish met with failure. It is relatively easy to induce any of the annual fishes to produce fertile eggs. The eggs are large, hard, and transparent, making it easy to determine that the fish have spawned. In the past, embryos developed in the eggs, but usually they failed to hatch. The few that did hatch produced weak or deformed babies.

It has been discovered that the eggs of annual fishes actually *need* a period of partial drying. Aquarists have found that if the eggs are kept in damp soil or moist peat moss for several weeks, the eggs hatch within hours or even minutes after they are returned to water. Young pearl fish have tremendous appetites, and they grow at an unbelievable rate. Within them there appears to be a rapid time clock that drives them to complete growth and reproduction in the brief time allotted to them. If they are kept in an aquarium beyond their natural life span, they become senile, humpbacked, shrivelled and soon die.

Aquarists have made good use of the annual fishes' unique life cycle in order to distribute them around the world. The eggs are collected and placed in damp peat moss. Sealed in an airtight container, they can be airmailed any place.

A few years ago annual fishes gave rise to a commercial venture that was called "Instant Fish." Eggs of annuals were placed in damp peat moss and sealed in plastic bags. The purchaser was instructed to place the contents of the bags in water and just watch his "Instant Fish" appear. However, the venture was not very successful, because there is a limit to how long the eggs can be stored, and it takes considerable skill to rear the young. But the scheme did attract a lot of attention while it lasted.

The annual fishes are fascinating to keep, and as a group, they are perhaps the prettiest freshwater fishes in the world.

13 »• *The Mosquito Fish*

Two fishes are called "mosquito fish" because they are widely known for their ability to eat mosquitos in the wild. The mosquito fish referred to here, *Heterandria formosa,* is so called because it is not much larger than a mosquito larva. It is the smallest fish found in North America and is one of the smallest fishes in the world. Females are fully grown at one inch and mature males measure only three-fourths of an inch. *Heterandria* is common from the Carolinas south to Florida and up the Gulf Coast.

Mosquito fish are very pretty in a quiet way. Both sexes are green, with a black line running from the eye to the base of the tail. A number of less distinct vertical bands cross the body. The male fish's dorsal fin has a black spot with red edging.

Mosquito fish are among the world's smallest fishes. The male (left) measures only three-quarters of an inch.

Like its cousin the guppy, *Heterandria* is a live-bearer, but unlike the guppy, *Heterandria* babies are born at a rate of two or three a day over a period of about ten days. Parents do not eat their young if there are plenty of floating plants.

Mosquito fish are ideal for the person who would like to keep fishes but cannot spare the room for an aquarium, because these diminutive creatures are happy in a gallon jar. With a little gravel on the bottom and some floating plants, mosquito fish are perfectly content to live in a wide-mouth gallon jar, producing babies as if they had a pond instead of a jar.

For many years *Heterandria formosa* was thought to be the smallest fish in the world. Then several fishes even smaller were discovered. *Pandaka pygmaea*, of the Philippines, measures only three-eighths of an inch fully grown. At the present time it holds the record for smallness. Nevertheless, the mosquito fish is the smallest fish likely to be seen in an aquarium.

14 »• *The Guppy*

WHILE goldfish have been kept as pets for hundreds of years, the tropical-fish hobby owes its great success to the comical little guppy—the first "tropical" fish to gain widespread popularity. After more than half a century of cultivation, the guppy is still the most popular tropical aquarium fish. More than a few aquarists have been introduced to the hobby by a gift of guppies from a friend. In his book, *Exotic Aquarium Fishes*, William T. Innes refers to the guppy as the "missionary fish," because it has made so many converts to the aquarium hobby. But what could be unusual about a fish so common as the common guppy?

The guppy has been introduced to so many places throughout tropical America that it is not certain just what the original habitat of this fish was. However, most scientists believe that the

A pair of guppies much like the wild guppies found in northern South America and Trinidad. It is difficult to believe that fancy guppies, such as the veiltail guppy, have been developed from fish like these.

guppy's original home territory was Venezuela, Trinidad, and the Guianas. This fish is extremely plentiful in these countries. For instance, every drainage ditch in the city of Georgetown, Guyana, teems with guppies.

Credit for discovering the guppy is generally given to the Reverend John Lechmere Guppy, who is supposed to have collected specimens in Trinidad in 1866. But even of this bit of guppy history there is some doubt.

Guppies are members of the family Poeciliidae, the livebearers. Instead of laying eggs, the females of this family give birth to fully developed baby fish. Since the eggs of all animals must be fertilized by sperms from the male before they can develop, it is apparent that guppies (and the other live-bearers) must have some means of fertilizing the eggs while they are still within the female. Nature accomplishes this nicely. When a young male guppy begins to mature, its flat anal fin slowly transforms into a hollow tube, called a gonopodium. Through his gonopodium, the male is able to inject sperms into the female's anal opening (in front of the anal fin). Once she receives the sperm, the female is able to store them for as long as six months, using them to fertilize each group of eggs. Under good conditions, a fully mature female guppy will produce fifty or more young every five weeks. At this rate, a female guppy might produce two thousand young in her lifetime! Of course, not all of the babies survive. The parents eat many of them, and many are eaten by other fishes. Even so, it is not difficult to understand why the guppy is the most plentiful tropical aquarium fish.

From the beginning of guppy culture, it was noted that males showed great variety in fin shapes and colors. No two wild male guppies were ever exactly alike. Through the years guppy fanciers have carefully selected until there are now more guppy varieties than could possibly be described here. Literally every color is seen on male guppies. There is even one variety, the golden guppy, in which both sexes are yellow all over.

Several guppy varieties are worth noting here, however. Some males have beautiful swordlike extensions on their tails. The extension may be on the top or the bottom. It will come as no surprise that these are called swordtail guppies. In another variety, there is a sword extending from both edges of the tail. These are called lyretails. Still another variety produces males with an iridescent green netlike pattern over the tail fin and body. These are lace guppies.

But the aristocrat of guppy varieties is the veiltail guppy, prize specimens of which have sold for more than $100 a pair. In

Male lyretail guppies have long extensions from the top and bottom of the tail fin.

the veiltail the tail has been developed into a broad triangle, sometimes as long as the fish's body. The dorsal fin extends back like a long plume. Veiltails come in many exquisite colors.

The king of guppy breeders is Henry Kaufman, of Trenton, New Jersey. Mr. Kaufman's veiltail guppies are known the world over as the finest money can buy. Kaufman has won so many world championships, national and local contests with his guppies that he no longer enters them in competition (much to the relief of other guppy breeders, no doubt).

So popular is the guppy that there are national, international, and local guppy breeders associations. These organizations exchange information, set standards for prize guppies, and sponsor guppy contests.

The guppy may be plentiful, but it is hardly fair to refer to it as the *common* guppy.

This magnificent male veiltail guppy was awarded "best of show" in a contest.

15 »• *The Wagtail Platy*

AQUARISTS are no different than other people in most respects. In general they have the typical attitude that uncommon things are the most desirable. For this reason a number of substantial tropical-fish importing firms go to great lengths to spend large sums of money to secure for aquarists exotic fishes from the Upper Amazon, the interior of equatorial Africa and Southeast Asia. While there are some beautiful fishes in our own waters, aquarists insist upon the exotic.

One notable exception is a fish that does not exist in the wild anywhere in the world. The wagtail platy was created by accident in the New York City laboratory of a distinguished biologist.

The late Dr. Myron Gordon was a widely acclaimed authority on the inheritance of cancer. Much of his experimental work was done with platyfishes, which are native to Central America. Dr. Gordon made a number of trips to Central American countries in search of fishes that had tumors or at least looked to him as though they might produce tumors.

One group of native platies brought back to the laboratory by

The wagtail platy was created unintentionally in a laboratory experiment. The gray area in the abdomen of the larger fish (left) is caused by developing embryos. The fish on the right is shown to be a male by its pointed anal fin.

Dr. Gordon had black edges on the top and bottom of their tail fins. He called them comet platies.

Writing in *The Aquarium,* August 1940, Dr. Gordon said, "When first we discovered the 'comet' platy in Mexico, we thought we had just another genic variety of the platyfish's great natural stock of patterns. While the black margined tail of the 'comet' was of interest to me in the study of fish genetics, the tropical fish dealer could not see any commercial success for it; and, I confess, neither did I."

However, when the biologist crossed his comet platies with some of the varieties in his laboratory, he was amazed. The babies produced had jet black fins and lips, with a scattering of black on the body. Here was a variety that would appeal to aquarists, which he named the wagtail platy. By careful selection, the strain was further refined until the black on the bodies was largely eliminated. Wagtails were crossed with golden platies and red platies, producing gold wagtails and red wagtails.

Geneticists now know that the wagtail pattern is caused by a genetic phenomenon similar to one that causes Siamese cats and Himalayan rabbits to have dark coloring on all of their extremities. To Dr. Gordon the wagtail platy was another tool to use in his research, but fortunately he shared his discovery with aquarists. Today wagtail platies can be purchased in virtually every store in the country that sells tropical fishes. They are nearly as common as guppies.

16 »• The Four-eyed Fish

IMAGINE a fish that sees out of water and in the water, *at the same time.* Scientists would be hard put to design an eye with such a capability. Yet nature has produced a fish with remarkable simultaneous aerial and aquatic vision. *Anableps,* called *cuatro-ojos* (Spanish for "four-eyes") in its native Central America and northern South America, has perhaps the most complicated eyes in the animal kingdom. While *Anableps* has only two eyes, in reality they function like four.

Anableps habitually swims at the surface of the water with half of its bulging eye above water and half beneath the surface. The upper half (above the water) looks through the air for birds and other enemies. At the same time the lower half looks through the water in search of food. To keep its eyes from drying out, *Anableps* frequently ducks its head under the water for an instant.

The four-eyed fish, ANABLEPS, *rests just beneath the surface of the water, with the upper half of its eye above water.*

The eyes of the four-eyed fish are a marvel of optical engineering. The iris of the eye is divided in two—precisely at the water line. Aquatic vision requires a thicker lens than aerial vision. *Anableps* has an egg-shaped lens, with the pointed end downward. Thus, light from the water passes through the long dimension of the lens, and light from the air passes across the short dimension. By this means, the same lens serves the purpose of forming two different images at the same time. Further, this fish's eye has two separate retinas, one on top and one on the bottom. Things seen from above the water focus on the lower retina, and things seen in the water focus on the upper retina.

The six-inch four-eyed fish is seldom imported to the United

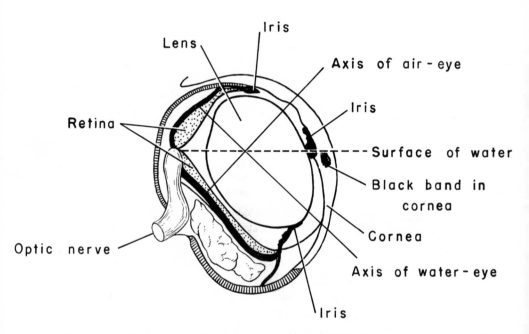

Drawing of the eye of ANABLEPS. *Images of things seen under the water are projected upon the upper retina, while things viewed above the water register on the lower retina. Other fishes have one continuous retina.*

States, but William A. Sternke, of Miami, Florida, has collected them, and has accomplished the extremely rare feat of breeding them in captivity. An article in *The Aquarium*, May 1957, gave an interesting account of how Mr. Sternke collected *Anableps* in Mexico.

"The fact that others had failed did not deter Sternke when Carlos Boner approached him with the idea of going to Mexico to get some four-eyes. Boner had been born in Mexico and knew the country well; in fact had brought back some four-eyes before, but had been unable to keep them alive. Deciding he'd like to try where others had failed, Sternke journeyed to the west coast of Mexico in March 1955, and Boner showed him where he had gotten his other *Anableps*. Sure enough, there were the *Anableps*, in a stream a stone's throw from the ocean which contained brackish water—and sewage. Sternke shook his head. Then he looked inland. He saw a swath of green cutting a winding pathway through the arid land. 'Let's go up there and get some *Anableps*,' Sternke said, pointing towards the mountains. There, in the fresh, clean waters of an ageless river that ran shallow through gorges and around mountains they found the incredible fish with the double eyes in each socket. Choosing a precipitous spot where the water was slow-moving, they had natives dam the river and they went to work with a seine. But this did not prove efficacious, as the fish simply leaped over the net. Finally they had to settle for the hand net. Sternke took care to select younger fish which were not full-grown, reasoning that they would be more adaptable to change. Thirty of these he shipped back by air to his Sunnyland Fish Farm in Miami, Florida, where Mrs. Sternke had the No. 1 outdoor pool ready for them. Despite expert care, 13 died within the first two weeks, but the remaining 17 survived and today present evidence of a triumph in fish-keeping."

Anableps is ordinarily a rather lazy fish, but it can move rapidly when it wishes to do so. When frightened it skitters across the surface of the water and occasionally leaps right out of the water. If it sees a smaller fish or some other morsel of food, it dives and catches its victims with some skill.

Mr. Sternke has observed the breeding habits of *Anableps* in captivity. Baby four-eyed fish are born alive. By means of a special anal fin (called a gonopodium), the male deposits his fertilizing sperms inside the female. The eggs remain inside the female until they hatch. A female *Anableps* has only two to five babies. For the size of the parents, the newborn are quite large: two inches. The abdomens of the babies are completely open for the first few days, as if the internal organs were all exposed. Then the abdominal opening gradually closes, without leaving a scar.

Anableps, the four-eyed fish, is a great novelty of the fish world. Although this olive-colored fish does not really have four eyes, an eye that sees two different images at once is remarkable enough.

17 »• *The Sea Horse*

APPARENTLY the quaint little sea horse has always been a curiosity for man. The remains of ancient buildings and sculpture show carvings of sea horses. The Greeks of antiquity attributed magical and healing powers to sea horses and ground dried seahorse bodies into powder for use in medicines to cure such diverse maladies as baldness and body pains. Pliny the Roman scholar gave a long list of ailments that supposedly could be cured by eating sea horses prepared in various ways.

In our own times, anyone who has ever visited the seashore has seen the dried and varnished bodies of sea horses that have been made into pins. But anyone whose knowledge of the sea horse is limited to a pin for a girl's sweater knows no more about these fascinating little creatures than an archaeologist knows of ancient Egyptian culture from a mummified body in a museum. Now that the life history of the sea horse is well known, these stiff little fishes have become more of a curiosity than ever.

While there are about twenty-five species of sea horses found in the marine waters of the world, only eight are native to United States coastal waters, and not all of these are found in a single location. Different species occur along the Pacific and Atlantic coasts. Three American species are commonly seen in aquariums: *Hippocampus erectus*, of the Atlantic Coast, *H. kuda* of the Pacific, and *H. zosterae*, found on the Florida coast and in the Gulf of Mexico.

Curiously, the scientific name for sea horse, *Hippocampus*, is a combination of the Greek words *horse* and *sea monster*. To the ancient Greeks hippocampus was a lengendary sea monster that had the appearance of a horse. How the sea horse could resemble a sea monster is something of a mystery, since the largest one ever found measured only eighteen inches, tip to tip, and most kinds average less than six inches.

By far the most popular sea horse with aquarists is the dwarf sea horse, *Hippocampus zosterae*, which fully grown measures only one and a half inches. Dwarf sea horses can be kept under conditions that would kill other kinds. They need only a small aquarium, and they can tolerate sea water that has been diluted with as much as 40 percent fresh water. Since they can be shipped in a small amount of water, collectors in Florida have developed substantial mail-order businesses with them.

Of a number of peculiar sea-horse characteristics, the most bizarre is the fact that the *male* mothers the young. Male sea horses have a pouch on their underside, into which the female deposits her eggs. The male arranges the eggs in neat rows among the folds of his pouch, and there they remain until they are finally expelled as perfect tiny replicas of their parents.

Sea horses are familiar to everyone, but few people know that the male sea horse carries the eggs in a pouch in his abdomen.

Incubation of the eggs may vary from a few days to a few weeks, depending on the species and the temperature of the water. At the time of birth the father appears to undergo labor pains much like those of the higher animals, including man. At each contraction, one or several babies are forced out until all are born.

Father sea horses sometimes suffer a serious ailment during pregnancy. Occasionally one or more of the embryos die in the pouch. As the dead embryo decays, a bubble of gas develops in the pouch and grows larger until the sea horse is forced to float at the surface. Experienced aquarists can sometimes save their pets by pressing the bubble out, but in nature the stricken fathers doubtless either die or in their helpless condition are eaten by larger fishes.

Sea-horse courtship is a delight to those who like to read human qualities into animals. Details differ from species to species, but in general, the male swims after and around likely females. In his zeal, he may even pursue another male. When a responsive female is found, the couple swims around together, sometimes even entwining their tails as they swim, for all the world looking like affectionate humans holding hands.

At last, the two face each other, and by means of a short ovipositor, the female quickly injects her eggs into the opening at the top of the male's pouch. The act is completed when the female has given up all of her eggs or when the male's pouch is full. Afterwards the female shows no further interest in her spouse or her young.

But these unique breeding habits are not their only peculiarities. Sea horses have no scales. Instead they are covered with tough bony plates that provide a sort of protective armor. Attached to the armor are only three fins. (Typical fishes have seven or eight fins.) It is no wonder then that sea horses are not very fast swimmers. By moving the dorsal fin on the back and the pectoral fin on either side beneath the head in rapid movements, the upright sea horse slowly moves forward or backward, up or down, left or right.

Because they are slow swimmers, sea horses depend upon camouflage for protection from their many enemies. Sea horses usually are colored to blend in with the grasses and seaweeds among which they live. Most are quite drab in appearance, but some species are beautifully colored. One kind of sea horse found along the coast of Australia is covered with long appendages that look very much like seaweed. In its natural setting this sea horse is virtually invisible. Even out of the water, it must be examined closely before one can be convinced that it really is a sea horse.

Camouflage aids sea horses in another valuable way: acquiring food. They sit quietly among the weeds waiting for baby fishes or other small animals to swim within catching range. As an intended victim swims into view, the sea horse slowly edges closer until its snout is less than an inch away. Then, with a sudden expansion of its gill covers, the prey is sucked into the sea horse's tubelike mouth.

A clever pair of eyes serve the sea horse well. Each moves independently of the other. While one eye may be looking upward at a potential enemy, the other may be looking downward at a bit of potential food.

Sea horses have gills that are unique with them and their close relatives, the pipefishes. Whereas most fishes have several layers of gills that look like little combs, the sea horse's gills are arranged in a solid mass with many tufts.

As might be expected, sea horses put their very flexible tails to good use. (In spite of drawings that you may have seen, sea horses cannot bend their tails backward. They are jointed in such a way that they are capable only of forward movement.) The natural home of sea horses is usually in tidal areas, where the movement of the tides at times creates fairly strong currents. With their poor ability to swim, sea horses would be swept to and fro if they had no way to stay put. This is where their tails are put to good use. When the water begins to move, they wind their tails around weeds or sticks. Even when the water is quiet sea horses can frequently be seen with their tails wound around something. So strong is the instinct to anchor themselves that when a baby sea horse is born, it almost immediately coils its tail around a weed or stick if one is nearby. Since father sea horses usually anchor themselves when they are ready to deliver, some object is usually close at hand.

As has already been stated, sea horses can be kept in aquariums. The larger ones, such as the common Atlantic species, require quite a lot of room and well aerated water, but the hardy little dwarf sea horse appears to be happy in as little as a gallon of water. A small many-branched stick should be placed in the container to enable the sea horses to satisfy their instinct to hang on with their tails. Of course, the water should be sea water, but this is no problem even far inland, because there are a number of good synthetic sea-water preparations available that can be mixed with ordinary tap water.

An aerator stone should be provided, even though it presents a minor hazard to male dwarf sea horses, which sometimes get bubbles caught in their pouches as they swim through the stream of air. The gentle movement of water created by the airstream is beneficial.

Feeding sea horses is a simple matter, thanks to the brine shrimp, a tiny animal found in salt ponds and the Great Salt Lake of Utah. Dust-fine brine shrimp eggs can be purchased at any pet store. Placed in salt water, the eggs hatch in about twenty-four hours. Sea horses thrive on newly-hatched brine shrimp, which stay alive in an aquarium until they are eaten. The larger species of sea horses also like baby guppies, but few aquarists have the heart to use guppies as food.

Dwarf sea horses readily produce babies in an aquarium, but they are very difficult to keep alive. Despite the most skillful attempts at rearing them, the tiny babies usually die one at a time until none is left. Even so, the babies are delightful while they last.

18 »• *The Banded Chaetodon*

THE colorful little banded chaetodon, or banded sunfish, which occurs in acid streams and ponds along the Atlantic Coast from southern New Jersey to northern Florida, is a highly-prized aquarium fish. Chaets (pronounced KEETS) have been popular for at least fifty years. The rest of the fishes in this book are included because of some unusual attribute, but the banded chaetodon is unusual only because it is one native fish that is popular with aquarists.

Chaetodons are dwarf members of the sunfish family. Their well-known cousins include smallmouth and largemouth bass, bluegills (bream in the South), pumpkinseed sunfish, and several others. In general shape, they look much like their cousins. But unlike most of their cousins they are peaceful in an aquarium. In good condition, chaetodons have six black vertical bands, one of them running through the eye, which is red. The front edges of the dorsal and ventral fins àre bright orange and black.

In at least one state, New Jersey, chaetodons have been collected so much that a law was passed for their protection. Some aquarists obtain a special collecting permit each year from the New Jersey Conservation Department. For them, spring collecting trips have become family affairs to which all look forward. Using two-man seines, they collect many chaetodons in a few hours. Only a few choice specimens are carried home, and the rest are returned to the pond unharmed.

Chaetodons occasionally are bred in aquariums, but not much is known about their breeding habits. The one personal experience the author had with breeding this fish cannot be called typical. A group of chaetodons had been collected in March, while the pond water was still very cold. As it happened, the fish were in breeding condition, waiting only for the water to warm sufficiently. Stimulated by the warmth of the fish room, the chaetodons spawned within a day. In this case, they scattered their eggs among some fine-leaf plants. The eggs hatched.

But it seems more likely that chaetodons generally spawn in typical sunfish fashion. Other sunfishes fan a depression in the sandy bottom of shallow water, in which the eggs are laid and fertilized. The parents guard the "nest" with great courage.

Chaetodons are even more popular in Germany than they are

The little banded sunfish or chaetodon is found along the east coast of the United States from New Jersey southward. It is the only native North American fish that has gained wide popularity with aquarists.

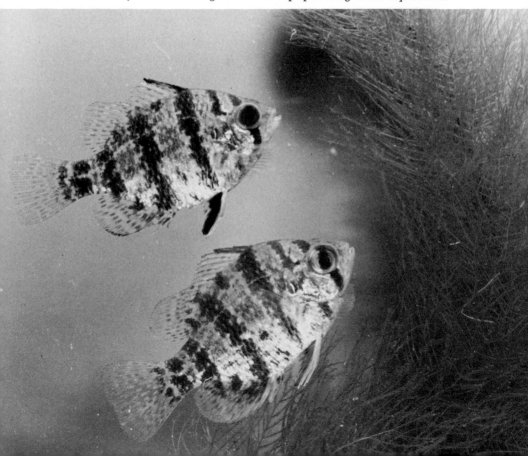

in the United States. German aquarists have considerable success breeding them. In fact, if you ever see chaetodons for sale in a tropical-fish store, they undoubtedly were imported from Germany, as it is against the law to sell wild ones in the United States.

19 »• *The Archer Fish*

ALTHOUGH it has no bow and arrows, the archer fish, *Toxotes*, must surely be one of the best marksmen in the animal world.

When reports began coming back from Southeast Asia in the eighteenth century of a fish that commonly shot down its insect food, scientists doubted that such a fish could exist. Then the American naturalist Dr. Hugh M. Smith was sent to the Far East in the 1920's as a fisheries consultant to the kingdom of Siam (now Thailand). In Siam, Dr. Smith had the opportunity to study the archer fish in the wild and in captivity. He observed the fish in action and removed all doubt as to its ability. The archer fish can and does, as a matter of habit, shoot down insects with drops of water. Later Dr. Smith and the Stanford University ichthyologist, Dr. George S. Myers, studied preserved archer fishes and learned exactly how the archer fish accomplishes its marksmanship.

Archer fishes are equipped with a groove running from the back to the front along the roof of the mouth. When the fish's tongue is placed against the roof of the mouth, a straight tube is formed. The archer spies an insect on an overhanging branch, swims up as close as it can, and places its lips just above the surface of the water. The gill covers are closed forcefully while the tip of the tongue covers the end of the groove. When the tip is relaxed, out spurts a stream of water with enough force to propel the drops several feet. If the first shot should miss, the

Even without its unique shooting ability, the archer fish would be a popular aquarium pet.

archer continues shooting until the insect is brought down.

The archer fish's ability to shoot at objects above the water is a most impressive adaptation in itself, but there is another aspect that has the scientists baffled. When we look into water at an angle, the objects we see in the water are not where they appear to be. As light passes from air into water, or vice versa, the light rays are bent. Human archers who shoot arrows at fishes in the water know that they must aim several feet under the fish if they

The people of Singapore have honored the archer fish by representing it on a postage stamp. TOXOTES JACULATOR *is the scientific name for this fish, which is shown shooting drops of water at a dragonfly which rests on a plant above the surface of the water.*

are to hit it. Somehow the archer fish also knows that the insects it sees are not really where they appear to be, and it compensates for this optical illusion with a high degree of accuracy.

Thus, the archer fish is freed from the fierce competition for food that often goes on in the water. With a squirt it reaches out for its food far beyond the limits of ordinary fishes.

Remarkable though the archer fish's ability is, sensational reports have tended to exaggerate the fish's shooting accuracy. Aquarists who have kept groups of archers have made reliable observations. The fish's first shot may be several inches from the target, but it quickly adjusts its mental sights and shoots again, this time closer or right on target. Archer fishes tend to swim in schools. When an insect is located, the whole school may open up with a barrage of squirts. Of course, when the insect falls, unless it is a very large one, only one fish gets the meal. Archer fishes also eat food in the water whenever they can get it. In fact, so long as there is plenty of food in the water, the archer will never use its shooting apparatus.

Ichthyologists cannot agree as to how many species of archer fishes exist. Some say there are four; others say six. To the layman who is accustomed to thinking of scientists as very precise people, such a situation seems surprising. But actually, disagreements of this sort are widespread throughout the biological world. These situations arise because in nature animals and plants differ from place to place. For example, the archer fishes of India may differ in some respects from those in Thailand. But are they sufficiently different to be considered separate species? Or are they merely variations of the same species? Thus the biologists sometimes fail to agree.

Arguments over how many kinds of archer fishes exist are of little interest to aquarists, however, because only one species ordinarily is imported to the United States: *Toxotes jaculator.* This five-inch fish is common in the salt, brackish, and fresh waters of the East Indies. Even without its gift for shooting, this archer would be a desirable aquarium fish, because it is a handsome creature. Over a yellowish or cream-colored body it has six broad jet-black bands on its sides.

Archer fishes do well in an aquarium. They readily eat pieces of meat or fish and small worms that are placed in the water.

20 »• *Badis Badis*

IT seems strange that aquarists have never given a common name to a lovely three-inch fish from India. Most fishes have names that refer to their appearance or actions. Angelfish look like angels. Hatchet fishes are shaped like hatchets. Fighting fish fight. But aquarists always refer to this fish simply by its scientific name, badis (pronounced BAH-dis). Often badis is called the chameleon of the aquarium, however, and for good reason.

To compare badis with the chameleon is not quite fair to the fish, because, as a quick-change artist, badis has the chameleon beaten by far. The little American chameleon or anole (as it is more accurately called) changes from brown to green and back again, and that is all. But badis puts the chameleon to shame with its color gyrations.

Many fishes have the ability to alter their colors to some extent, but no other fish can change to so many colors in so short a period of time. Within a few minutes badis may turn from dark brown to a group of black, yellow, and red bands, and then to plain pink, or to many other colors and combinations. To add to badis's peculiarities, it is in the habit of remaining motionless for periods of time in all sorts of unusual, unfishlike positions.

Badis does well in an aquarium, if it is given plenty of live foods or any of the frozen fish foods that are available at any pet shop. It can be quite easily induced to breed, *if* you have a pair. The problem is getting a pair, for it is extremely difficult to tell males from females. The best way to be sure of having both sexes is to buy at least six fish. Mathematicians tell us that if we buy six fish of unknown sex, we are nearly 100 percent certain of obtaining both sexes. A mathematician once wrote an article in *The Aquarium* magazine explaining why this is so, but the logic of it escapes this author now.

When two badis begin to pair off and pay an unusual amount of attention to each other, they are removed to an aquarium of their own, assuming that they are male and female. An ordinary clay flowerpot is placed on its side in the aquarium. Actual spawning is preceded by much wrestling and much swimming after each other. All the while both fishes display colors even more dramatic than anything they had ever shown before. By the time the eggs are laid the male may be deep blue, and the female may be nearly white.

A pair of BADIS BADIS *prepares to spawn inside a broken earthenware jar. The darker male is on the left. Note that the female's abdomen is enlarged with eggs.*

Badis spawn in nature on the underside of some object like a stone or a log. In this rare photograph the male fish is embracing the female while she lays her eggs. A number of eggs are fastened to the surface.

About one hundred eggs are deposited on the inside upper surface of the flowerpot. Once the spawning is completed, the male drives the female away. He assumes a position inside the pot and fans fresh water across the eggs. The eggs hatch in a few days. A well-fed pair of badis may spawn as often as every two weeks.

21 »• *The Amazon Leaf Fish*

THE leaf fish of the Amazon and the Guianas is a superb camouflage artist. With colors varying from dark brown to gray, it drifts aimlessly through the water looking remarkably like one of a million real leaves in the stream. So good is its camouflage that even in a net with assorted dead leaves and twigs, it is likely to be returned to the water unseen—unless it moves.

Dark coloring is only one in a whole bagful of camouflage tricks of the leaf fish. The body, with its margin of jagged fins, is a perfect leaf outline. From the eye radiate several dark lines resembling the veins of a leaf. Many leaf fish have a quarter-inch-long flap of skin protruding from their lower lip that looks much like the stem of a leaf. And to complete the deception, the only fins that normally move—the pectorals and the rear tips of the dorsal and anal fins—are transparent, nearly invisible when in motion. Further, leaf fish frequently swim at an unfishlike head-down angle.

In its natural setting of dead leaves and sticks, the brown leaf fish is nearly invisible. Many of these fish imitate leaves so effectively that they even have a "stem" extending from the chin.

While this clever camouflage gives the three-inch leaf fish wonderful protection from larger predatory fishes, the main value of the camouflage is as an aid in capturing smaller fishes. The leaf fish may drift with the current until an unsuspecting smaller fish swims near, or it may sidle ever so slowly up to a fish until its mouth is almost touching. Then, in a lightning-fast motion, the lower jaw swings down, and an unbelievably huge tube-like mouth unfolds and swings out, creating a suction that draws the unsuspecting victim in. With a gulp, the hapless fish is gone. Fully extended, the mouth is as long as the fish's head. Occasionally, the leaf fish extends its cavernous mouth for no apparent reason, as if it were yawning out of boredom.

Leaf fish are good parents. Eggs are usually deposited on the underside of a living leaf or on a stone. After the fish give much affectionate attention to each other, the female carefully deposits her eggs and the male fertilizes them. Each egg is attached to the leaf or stone by a short thread. Hence, the large glassy eggs are all raised slightly off the spawning site.

The male leaf fish stays close to the eggs, carefully fanning water over them. They hatch in about two days, but the babies remain attached to the spawning site by the egg thread for another week. Once they are free-swimming, baby leaf fish act much like their parents, remaining still most of the time. At first, young leaf fish eat small aquatic animals, but by the time they have grown to a half inch, they are able to eat small fishes the size of baby guppies.

Leaf fish do well in an aquarium, but they prefer to eat live fishes. Guppies are eagerly eaten, but this can be costly food. In some places, like the southern states, there is an abundance of small native fishes that can be caught and fed to the leaf fish.

22 »• *The Mouthbrooder*

WHILE some fishes show absolutely no interest in their young once the eggs are laid (except to eat them), others are devoted parents. In a number of species either parent or both of them may care for both eggs and young until they are large enough to fend for themselves. The parents of certain African and Asian fishes show a sacrificial devotion to their young that must surely surpass the devotion of any other members of the animal kingdom. The mother or father mouthbrooder carries the eggs and babies around in his or her mouth.

One species of African mouthbrooder, *Tilapia mossambica*, has been widely distributed throughout the tropical world because it is fairly good to eat, and it can live and multiply profusely in ponds and rice paddies where other fishes of equal size would die. *Tilapia* has become an important food item in many protein-starved areas of the world.

However, the mouthbrooder best known to aquarists is the Egyptian mouthbrooder, *Haplochromis multicolor*, a fish that grows to only about three inches. Males of this species are very attractive, with blue, white, and reddish markings over the body and fins. The females are less brightly marked.

With good feeding, it is not difficult to get these fish to spawn in an aquarium. At spawning time the male Egyptian mouthbrooder digs a depression in the sand by fanning his tail. He coaxes the female into his "nest." There the female deposits a few eggs and after the male fertilizes them, she picks them up in her mouth. More eggs are laid in this manner until there are one hundred or more—all in the mother's large mouth. For two weeks no sign of the young is seen, and then one day the whole brood is released to try their fins. At first they venture forth for

A pair of mouthbrooders preparing to spawn. The more colorful male is on the left and the egg-laden female is on the right.

only short periods. All during this incubation period the mother can be seen pumping water over her children, through her mouth and gill covers, and she occasionally rearranges them within her mouth.

For another three weeks or more the young hover about the mother's mouth. At the first sign of danger they dart into her mouth for protection. At last the youngsters become so large that the mother's mouth no longer can hold them. From then on they must manage on their own. In fact, even their own mother becomes a danger to them, for once the young are too large for her mouth, she may eat them.

All during this time (about five weeks) the mother refrains from eating *anything*. Her shriveled body is a pathetic sight. In some cases the female starves herself to death, but usually a week or two of good feeding restores her to normal proportions.

The instinct to refrain from eating at breeding time is very strong in these fish. One aquarist reported in *The Aquarium* magazine of July 1944: "During the middle of April I purchased a pair of these fish and put them in a seven-gallon community tank which contained several other pairs of fish. On May 6th I noticed that the female mouthbreeder was refusing to eat, and that her mouth was enlarged, so I removed her to another aquarium. Within a week the little fish could be seen very plainly in her mouth, and on May 18th I discovered them out

Even after the baby mouthbrooder fish have hatched and become free-swimming, they hover about the mother's mouth, ready to swim inside at the first sign of danger.

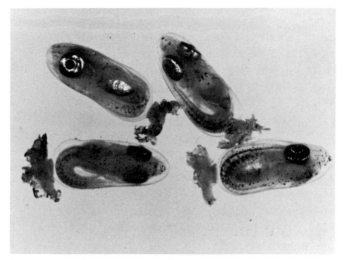

*Fully developed mouthbrooder babies, curled inside
the transparent egg membrane.*

For several days after they have hatched, newborn mouthbrooders
(and many other fishes) have a large yolk sac, from which they receive
nourishment until they grow strong enough to catch their own food.

swimming in the water; but as soon as I moved closer to the aquarium they all swam back into the mother's mouth. The next day they were out again and when I approached the aquarium the mother made no motion toward storing them back in her jaws. She appeared to be through with her parental duties, and so I removed her from the young back into the community tank. However, she refused to take food and although I watched her for three weeks, she never took anything to eat. She became as thin as it was possible for her to be and last week she died." It was concluded that the aquarist had separated the mother from her babies too soon, and without them to carry through the entire brood period, she had just continued her fasting to the end.

The Egyptian mouthbrooder's parental devotion is certainly far above and beyond the call of duty.

23 » • *The Angelfish*

WITH its long wing-like fins, stately manner and distinctive markings, the angelfish is indeed an angel of the aquarium.

Some ichthyologists say that there are three distinct species of angelfish, but others say that there is only one species, with three varieties. However, all three are very similar, and so far as the aquarist is concerned, there is only one freshwater angelfish.

Angelfish have a rather wide distribution in the wild. They are common throughout the Amazon River and its tributaries, northward to Venezuela and the Guianas. Having once seen them in their native waters, it is apparent that they are well adapted to living where they do. Angelfish live along the shores of rivers and ponds, where masses of plants grow out of the water. With their high, thin proportions, angelfish can swim far in among the plants, where they are safe from larger fishes. The black vertical bands provide protective coloration so that they blend into their surroundings.

They have been produced in this country for so long that wild angelfish are only occasionally imported, and wild specimens are considered novelties.

Angelfish have interesting breeding habits, and they are very devoted parents. (They are members of the cichlid family, a group of fishes well known for their interesting breeding habits.)

It is not difficult to breed angelfish, if they are allowed to choose their own mates, and if they are well fed. Generally a piece of slate about three inches wide and a foot long is placed in the aquarium, leaning against one of the glass sides. If a broad-leaf plant is in the aquarium, the parents may prefer it to the slate.

The sexes in angelfish are very difficult to distinguish. The only really reliable difference is the swollen abdomen of the female as her eggs reach maturity. At breeding time, the female develops a short spawning tube (ovipositor). The spawning site (slate or leaf) is carefully cleaned by both parents. Then the female moves over the site and deposits a row of eggs, one egg at a time. The male follows and fertilizes them. More and more rows of eggs are placed until there may be two hundred or more on the site.

After the spawning is complete, both parents care for the eggs. Any speck of dirt is removed. Dead eggs are eaten before they can rot and damage the others. (Living angelfish eggs are transparent amber color, and dead eggs are white.) The first babies appear in two days or less, and they are attached to the spawning site by a short, sticky thread extending from the baby's head. The parents keep the babies together until they are free-swimming, and they sometimes move the babies from place to place.

If the parents are disturbed at any time, they are likely to eat the eggs or babies. Because of this risk, most aquarists remove the slate with the eggs to a gallon jar filled with water from the

Mature angelfish are handsome creatures.

aquarium. An airstone with a gentle stream of bubbles is placed beneath the eggs to substitute for the cleaning and fanning of the parents. Of course, this artificial method denies the aquarist the pleasure of observing the angelfish's family life, but it does eliminate the risk of the parents becoming cannibals. Away from the parents, the eggs are likely to be infected with a fungus disease; thus a few drops of fungus-killing chemical are usually added to the water in the jar.

Angelfish have the ability to turn their black bars on or off at will. If they are severely frightened they may turn pale and lie flat on the bottom for a while as if in a faint. The best time to see angelfish without their bars is at night, after all lights have been turned off. When the light is turned on, the fish are likely to be nearly white, and they may be resting on the bottom. The dark bars quickly return, however. (Many people have wondered if fishes sleep. The answer is that many fishes apparently do.)

Several interesting varieties of angelfish have been developed by skillful selective breeding. One, the veiltail angelfish, was developed in Germany and was first brought to the United States by the aquarist William Sternke in 1957. In the veiltail angelfish, all of the fins are two or three times longer than the fins of normal angelfish. Another variety, a jet-black fish, is truly magnificent. At its best even the fins are completely black.

Once the veiltail angelfish and the black angelfish were established, it was only a matter of time until the two were combined. Black veiltail angelfish are now available in nearly every tropical-fish store.

In any of its varieties, the angelfish would surely be among the five most popular aquarium fishes. No community aquarium is complete without a few.

Aquarists in Germany have developed the veiltail angelfish, in which all of the fins are several times longer than normal.

Jet black angelfish have been developed from the wild type. They make an interesting contrast in an aquarium of colorful fishes.

24 »• *The Discus Fish*

WHEN discus fish (*Symphysodon discus*) from the tributaries of the Amazon River were first introduced to American aquarists in 1933, they created a sensation. For years afterward, the discus was regarded as the king of aquarium fishes. Even today, many aquarists regard it as the choicest tropical fish available.

It is easy to understand why the mature discus fish should be regarded as the most regal of aquarium fishes. They swim about with a noble bearing and a touch of shyness. Fully grown (about six inches), and in good condition, they possess great beauty, both of bearing and coloration. Viewed from the front discus are extremely thin for their size, but from the side they are nearly round. (Hence, the name *discus*, which is Latin for plate or dish.) Their basic body color is brown. Brilliant blue bars cover both dorsal and anal fins, and the bars extend onto the back and stomach. Dorsal, ventral, and anal fins are edged in bright red. There is a variety of discus, from Lake Tefe, Brazil, that has bright metallic green or blue bars all over its fins and body. This variety is occasionally imported also.

Discus fish belong to a fish family called cichlids, which are known for the careful attention the parents give to their young. But even among the cichlids, discus fish are outstanding parents.

Because they prefer to choose their own mates, aquarists who hope to breed discus fish usually buy several specimens. When two fish are seen to pair off, the other discus are removed from the aquarium.

It is nearly impossible to distinguish male discus from females. As spawning time approaches, the female's abdomen becomes slightly enlarged because of the eggs she is carrying. A few days before she lays her eggs, the female develops a short tube, or

There are several beautiful kinds of discus fish that are considered by ichthyologists to be distinct species. The species of discus shown here is covered with brilliant metallic blue-green stripes.

ovipositor, just in front of her anal fin.

In most respects, discus fish spawn like angelfish. The eggs hatch in about five days, during which time the parents guard the eggs, fan them with their fins, and work them over with their mouths, apparently cleaning them. At first, the tiny, sliverlike fry remain nearly motionless on the spawning site, unless the parents move them to a new location—which they often do.

At the age of four days the young become free-swimming. It is here that most attempts at discus breeding came to an end in the past, because the parents were usually removed at this point for fear they might eat their own babies. The young, however, began to die off a few at a time, until there were none left. An aquarist who succeeded in rearing six young from a spawning of two hundred eggs was considered to have achieved a great accomplishment. Then several aquarists made a startling discovery. They found that the baby discus eat something from the sides of their parents. Thus, to remove the parents was inevitably to starve the babies.

One of the first to observe baby discus feeding from their parents was Gene Wolfsheimer, a gifted aquarist-photographer from California, who took some of the photographs in this book.

Writing in *The Aquarium,* January 1957, Mr. Wolfsheimer said, ". . . the baby discus immediately went up to the sides of the parents. They seemed to stick very closely and at this time were observed most carefully. . . . The young fish were nursing off the sides of the parents. The protective slime that covers the sides of the adults also supplied the first and only food for the babies. It was an experience I had yet to witness during my fish-breeding career—to watch the fry head into the huge sides of the parents, apparently dig its head in, jerk to one side with a tearing motion and go back to do this again and again. When there seemed to be a scarcity of this food on one of the parents, the fry would migrate to the other . . . At the moment about 125 young discus . . . are growing up . . ."

Discus fish belong to a group of fishes long known for their devotion to their offspring, but not until recently was it discovered that both discus parents actually feed their young with substances produced in the parents' skin. Several babies can be seen here picking food from their parents' sides.

Later studies by scientists showed that there are special food-producing cells or glands in the parents' skins. As the babies reach the free-swimming age, they cling to the side of one parent, feeding while they cling. When one parent grows weary of the babies, it shakes itself and all the babies are transferred to the side of the other parent. For several weeks the babies continue receiving nourishment from the parents. Gradually they become less and less dependent upon the parents, until finally they are completely on their own. Baby discus may be nearly a half-inch long before they become completely independent.

Young discus bear little resemblance to their parents. For the first few months they are elongated, like most fishes. But by the time they reach the size of a dime, they are nearly as rounded as the adults.

25 »• *The Marine Clownfish or Anemone Fish*

IN general, the fishes from the seas of the world are much more difficult to keep alive and healthy in an aquarium than the freshwater fishes. A notable exception is an unbelievably brilliant little fish common to the coral reefs of the South Pacific Ocean, the clownfish, *Amphiprion percula*. So long as it is kept well fed, and so long as the salt content is kept close to that of the ocean, the clownfish appears to be perfectly satisfied with a captive life.

The clownfish referred to here has a number of close relatives, all of them of similar habits, and all of them with beautiful coloring, but *Amphiprion percula* is chosen to represent the group because it is the species most often sold to aquarists. *A. percula* grows to about two inches and is marked with orange and white vertical bars so vivid that they look as though they had been painted on with enamel. All of the fins are orange. The edges of the fins are black. A thin black line separates the orange and white bands. Altogether, the clownfish is a breathtaking animal.

What makes the clownfish remarkable in its habits is its close association with lower animals called sea anemones, which look more like elegant flowers than animals. Sea anemones are primitive animals with a short trunk ending in a cluster of colorful tentacles with the appearance of flower petals. In the center of the tentacles there is a mouth, which opens into a hollow body cavity. In the anemone's tentacles are hundreds of tiny stinging cells capable of killing a fish with ease, but the little clownfish swims among the tentacles in perfect safety. Researchers in California have discovered that the mucus covering of the clownfish contains a substance that gives it protection from the anemone's stingers. When other fishes come in contact with a sea anemone's tentacles, the stinging cells pierce into the fish's side, propelled

Marine clownfish are remarkable for their habit of living among the poisonous tentacles of primitive animals called sea anemones.

by a springlike mechanism. But when the clownfish touches the tentacles, the anemone recognizes the mucus of its friend and holds back its deadly weapons.

Dr. Leonard Schultz, of the Smithsonian Institution, has studied sea anemones and clownfishes in their native Pacific waters. Dr. Schultz found that there is a mutually beneficial relationship between them. (Scientists call such a relationship *symbiosis*.) The clownfish receives protection from its enemies. When it is threatened by a larger fish, it swims among the tentacles, where the larger fish does not dare to go after it.

The sea anemone's benefit is in receiving some of its food from the fish. When the clownfish finds a piece of food, it swims to the anemone and deposits the food among the tentacles. The fish may collect and deposit a number of pieces of food before it begins to eat them. Then, at its leisure, and in the sanctuary of the anemone's tentacles, the clownfish eats its fill. The sea anemone moves any leftover scraps to its mouth, and eats them. Thus both animals find the relationship a very practical one.

Many observers have wondered how such a brightly colored fish could survive in nature because brightly colored fishes are easily seen by predators, but with its friend the sea anemone ever close to protect it, the clownfish has no worries.

26 »• *The Mudskipper*

"Is it a fish or a frog?" is a question asked by many a person viewing the slippery little mudskipper for the first time. Actually this comical creature is a fish that *thinks* it is a frog.

Along coastal beaches and estuaries from the Indian Ocean to the South Pacific, *Periophthalmus* may be seen in large numbers walking and hopping out of the water onto dry land or making its way up the tilted roots of mangrove trees. But *why* should a fish leave the water? The answer is simple enough. Through eons of experience the mudskippers have learned that just beyond the water's edge is an abundance of food—insects and small crustaceans—that is unavailable to the other fishes. Here the mudskipper can stalk and capture its food without the fierce competition that exists in the water. Three unique adaptations make it possible for this fish to leave its natural environment for periods of time.

The mudskipper uses its fins and tail for getting about on land. Its broad, flat ventral fins provide support for the fish to remain in an upright position. Two pectoral fins with exceptionally strong muscles provide the power for moving ahead. When the mudskipper walks, it pulls itself forward with a stroke of its pectorals. Then it balances itself with its ventral fins while the pectorals are moved forward for another "step." When the mudskipper is in a hurry, it skips ahead in short hops, propelled by its powerful tail. With its pectoral and ventral fins it can climb onto rocks and tree roots if the angle is not too steep. It is said that a mudskipper in a hurry can travel faster than a man can walk, and it doubtless can move more rapidly on land than in the water.

Most fishes quickly die out of water. They literally suffocate in the midst of abundant oxygen. Fishes get their oxygen through their moist skin and their gills, both of which quickly dry out in the air. But the little mudskipper has solved the problem of breathing out of water. In the first place, it somehow knows that its skin must be kept moist. It always tries to keep some part of its body wet. In shallow water in an aquarium, it frequently rolls over in the water like a dog. It may hop into and out of the water frequently, but even completely separated from water, the mudskipper can live as long as a day. It manages to keep the inside of its mouth and its gills moist enough for breathing long after the rest of its body has become as dry as leather.

Another helpful adaptation of the mudskipper is its bulging

The froglike mudskipper is at home in the water or out. This one is resting on a stone with only its tail in the water.

eyes. This must have impressed the naturalist Linnaeus, who gave the fish its scientific name *Periophthalmus*, which means "eyes that look all around." Mudskipper's eyes are unique in two ways. First, they function independently of each other. While one eye is looking up, the other may be looking down—or in any other direction. Second, the mudskipper's eyes are adapted to seeing at a distance. The eyes of fishes have spherical lenses that

The powerful pectoral fins used by the mudskipper for "walking" over land are apparent here. This fish's bulging eyes operate independently of each other.

limit clear vision to a few inches, but the mudskipper's lenses are equipped with muscles that can move the lenses close to the retina. Thus, *Periophthalmus* is able to focus on objects many feet away. These visual adaptations enable the fish to see and stalk its food and also to see and elude the shore birds that regard it as a choice morsel of food.

In *The Aquarium* magazine, November 1932, the late Philadelphia ichthyologist Henry W. Fowler tells of his first meeting with mudskippers in the wild: "About the extensive mud flats of the Indo Australian Archipelago, mudskippers are met with in perhaps their greatest profusion. This is usually near lagoons or tidal estuaries, especially about or near mangrove flats. My first acquaintance with it was in the coral reef islands in the Java Sea. Though only a few were found at first, I saw perhaps more of its ability to skip about on land and over the water, than most any place visited. Its method of skipping over the surface of shallow pools, by leaping a foot or more, was most interesting. Each time it alighted on the surface of the water with a little splash and soon progressed from about 5 to 20 feet. Its objective was nearly always toward some goal above the water. Often it would finally alight on a mangrove root and then crawl or wriggle up until well above the water line. Sometimes it would jump from one root to another, often with fins expanded, though its movements through the air are so difficult to follow I was not always sure of this. On the soft, wet mud it would crawl, wriggle or skip about with apparent abandon, though doubtless in search of minute insects or crustaceans which were scarcely visible. Here it was found in numbers of a dozen or more, though appearing scattered and not in schools. About the mangrove roots it is usually impossible to catch any."

The species of mudskipper most commonly imported is olive-colored, with blue spots on the head and fins. It averages around four inches in length.

Mudskippers can be kept in aquariums without too much difficulty. They like lots of room. The aquarium should be covered to keep them from jumping out. Water should be half seawater and half freshwater, about an inch deep and kept at about 80 degress Fahrenheit. A sand beach and sticks or stones should be provided. They will eat insects, small worms, and insect larvae.

The mudskipper does a good job of acting more like an amphibian than a fish.

27 »• *The Climbing Perch*

THE climbing perch is not a perch, and it does not climb, but it is nonetheless an unusual creature. This fish is said to have been given its common name by a nineteenth-century Dutch naturalist travelling in India who saw one in a tree. How the fish got in the tree is a mystery, because the climbing perch is not equipped to climb anything.

Found from India to the Philippines, *Anabas testudineus* is a popular performer at fish shows and public aquariums, for it is always willing to demonstrate its ability to walk on dry land. When the fish wishes to walk, it spreads its gill covers, which are equipped with spines that aid in gaining a "footing." Then, with a laborious rolling motion, it moves forward by grasping with its gill covers and moving its tail.

Most apparently odd characteristics have some practical purpose, and the climbing perch's ability to walk doubtless has enabled it to survive. *Anabas* lives in areas in which ponds are likely to dry up at certain times of the year. When a pond becomes too low or stagnant for the climbing perch, it just strikes out across country in search of a better pond. Surely many of them die before they reach water again, but enough of them succeed to insure the survival of the species.

The brownish climbing perch is a member of the family of labyrinth fishes, to which the well-known Siamese fighting fish also belongs. When labyrinth fishes breathe, they go to the surface and take in a mouthful of air, which is forced through a many-chambered breathing apparatus in the head and then passed out through the gill covers. With this unique means of breathing, the climbing perch and other labyrinth fishes can live in stagnant ponds that would be the death of other fishes.

With its covering of thick skin and large scales, the climbing perch resists drying out on its travels.

The late ichthyologist Dr. Hugh M. Smith had the opportunity to watch climbing perch in their native lands. He saw them walking across roads, over dusty areas, and through grass. He even saw them climb up steep banks and then at the end of the journey tumble back into another pond. Dr. Smith believed that *Anabas* had some sort of homing instinct or sense of where it wished to go. On one occasion he watched a native catch one and place it in a basket. When the basket was placed on the ground some distance away, the fish climbed out of the basket and returned to the pond from which it had been removed.

Climbing perch are quite easy to keep in an aquarium, because of their toughness and because of their small size (up to ten inches).

Climbing perch commonly move right out of the water onto dry land.

28 »• *The Fighting Fish of Siam*

THE betta or Siamese fighting fish, *Betta splendens,* is one of the best-known aquarium fishes, but many people know little about the interesting habits, characteristics, and background of this beautiful little fish from southeast Asia.

In the fighting fish we have a fine example of how people with virtually no knowledge of genetic principles can alter and improve a wild animal. The wild fish found in the ponds and streams of Thailand and neighboring countries bear little resemblance to the magnificent cultivated strains, which are surely among the most beautiful fishes in the world. Wild bettas are an overall brownish color, with short fins and a stocky, torpedo-shaped body. Through long selective breeding with the infinite patience of which only the Asian peoples are capable, the male fighting fish has developed flowing fins that may extend two inches beyond its two-inch body, and displaying many brilliant colors. In any pet store in the United States, fighting fish may be seen in albino, red, blue, green, near-blacks, and in any combination of these colors. The females retain the short fins of the wild type, but they occur in any of the above-mentioned colors.

The fighting ability of the betta has been greatly exaggerated, notwithstanding the fact that a healthy male fish is always ready for combat. Rarely do they fight to the death, although an occasional fish may die later from wounds that become infected. In Thailand the fighting fish is used for fish fights, much as fighting cocks are used in some parts of the world. However, neither wild fish nor the beautiful cultivated varieties are used for fighting. Special strains have been developed for their pugnacity, and it is said that the best fighters have long pedigrees.

Fish fights are staged in a specific way. Two owners bring their fish together in small jars. Upon sight of each other, the fish immediately go into a frenzy of excitement. Color intensifies, fins are spread, gill covers are opened wide, and the fish press their snouts against the glass in an attempt to get at each other. The men present watch all of this carefully, and on the basis of the fish's pre-fight performance they make wagers as to which will win. Then the two are placed together in a glass container. Immediately they square off. Fins are shredded and scales knocked loose. The two may lock jaws and roll about the container. At last one fish has enough of it and retreats to a corner in an attempt to get away. Those who have bet on the vanquished have lost their money. A fish is rarely killed. Both may require

Ordinarily the fins of the male Siamese fighting fish are relaxed, but upon seeing another fighting fish, a male will spread his fins and advance for an attack.

weeks to fully recover, and the fins may be permanently scarred. It is said that in the old days so intense was the betting that men would sometimes bet their whole families into slavery.

In fighting instinct the highly developed show fish of aquarium interest are faint shadows of their counterparts in Thailand. In the process of selecting bettas for their color and large fins, much of the will to fight has been lost. Even so, if two males are kept in the same aquarium, the flowing colorful fins will soon become shredded and torn. When a mirror is placed beside the aquarium, a male will attempt to do battle with his reflection. Because of the fighting instinct that does remain, male fighting fish are always reared in small individual containers. Because of a unique supplementary breathing apparatus, they are able to thrive in less than a pint of water.

Bettas belong to a group called the labyrinth fishes, all of which possess a many-chambered breathing structure in their heads. Bettas need not pump water through their gills to obtain oxygen as other fishes do. When the betta breathes, it goes to the surface and takes a mouthful of air, which it presses into its labyrinth apparatus and out through its gills. In nature this attribute makes it possible for bettas to live in oxygen-depleted stagnant, muddy pools, and in captivity it enables them to live in a container so small that it would quickly suffocate most other fishes. Although bettas do use their gills in the typical fish manner, they are not totally dependent upon them for their survival.

As if all of this were not enough attributes for one creature, the betta engages in one of the most charming mating rituals in the animal kingdom. When a healthy male fighting fish is placed in an aquarium with a female bearing ripe eggs, he at once turns on his color to its brightest, spreads his fins to their fullest, and begins to chase the female, who at first runs away. After a period of chasing, the male settles down to more serious business. Among some floating plants, or in an obscure corner, he builds a nest of tiny bubbles. The male goes to the surface for a mouthful of air, which is chewed to give it a strong mucous coating. Then it is deposited as a sturdy bubble at the nesting site. Again and again he repeats the process until the nest may be several inches broad and as much as half an inch high above the surface of the water. When the nest reaches a satisfactory size, or when the male's excitement reaches a pitch beyond his endurance, he heads toward the female, who has been cowering in a far corner. The male betta pushes, shoves, and coaxes the female into a position under the nest. If she is ready to spawn, she acquiesces to the male's forceful advances. In a position just under the nest, the male encircles the female's body with his own, and a few pinhead-size white eggs are expelled and fertilized by the male. Authorities are not agreed as to whether the male actually squeezes the eggs from the female or whether they are merely expelled in the moment of excitement, but photographs tend to show that they are released by the female without assistance from the male.

The eggs sink slowly toward the bottom. While the female remains motionless in an apparent swoon, the male picks the eggs up in his mouth and carefully tucks them into the bubble nest.

The embrace is repeated again and again, until as many as several hundred eggs are laid, the actual number varying with the size of the female and the vigor of the male. Once the spawning is completed, the male viciously drives the female away. If she cannot retreat far enough from the nest, she may be killed.

A male fighting fish goes about his paternal chores with admirable enthusiasm. The nest is guarded against intruders. If an egg falls from the nest, the male immediately tucks it back in. Bubbles are added until the nest may double in size.

In from twenty-four to forty hours (depending on the temperature) the eggs begin to hatch into tiny hair-thin fry. Looking across the bottom of the nest, it appears to be coated with fuzz

Upon completing construction of a nest of bubbles, the male fighting fish wraps himself about the female. This stimulates her to release a few small white eggs, which can be seen between the female's ventral fins in the photograph above. In the photograph at the right, taken several minutes later, eggs can be seen beside the female's abdomen, several more are slowly sinking to the bottom, and a number of others can be seen that were earlier tucked into the bubble nest by the male.

from the young fish hanging downward.

Within a few days the young begin to swim away from the nest. At first the father diligently puts them back into the nest as

fast as they swim free, but soon it becomes more of a chore than he can handle. Aquarists generally remove the father betta at this time, because he is likely to give up in frustration and devour the whole brood.

Isn't it strange that so pugnacious a fish should have such engaging reproductive habits! It is little wonder that the fighting fish from Siam did much to establish the tropical-fish hobby in the United States. Surely few other fishes have so many appealing qualities: masculine pugnacity, brilliant colors, ability to live in a small container, willingness to put on a delightful reproductive display in a small aquarium.

29 »• *The Kissing Gourami*

IT takes only a few words to tell about the unusual feature of the kissing gourami, but this fish is so amusing in its behavior that it is well worth the telling.

Humans are extremely fond of seeing human qualities in animals, whether the animals are really capable of those qualities or not. There is a specific word for our tendency to see human traits in animals: anthropomorphism. In the kissing gourami we have a wonderful opportunity to be anthropomorphic.

Kissing gouramis in an aquarium occasionally come together and touch their large, rubbery mouths together, like two lovers oblivious to anyone else in the world. Some kissers never do this, and others kiss continually. The actual reason for this highly entertaining action is not known. Aquarists are always a little disappointed to learn that the kissing almost certainly has nothing to do with affection. It may really be a way of showing aggression, or it may have something to do with the feeding habits of the fish, for they spend much of their time working their mouths over the bottom of the aquarium, over plants, and

Two kissing gouramis are caught in the act.

along the glass sides in search of food.

The kissing gourami, which is native to Southeast Asia and the East Indies, grows to about a foot long under ideal conditions, but in an aquarium it seldom exceeds six inches. There are two color varieties. The normal wild type is light green with about a dozen horizontal stripes on each side of the body. Much more

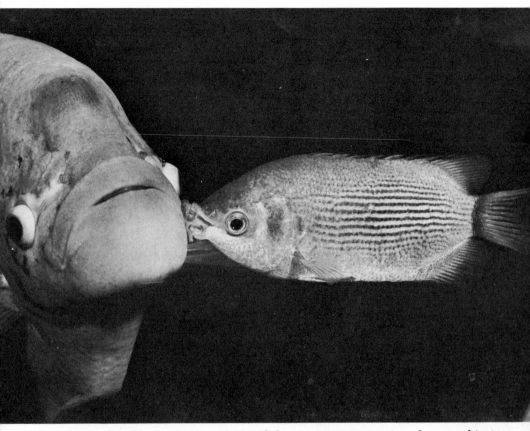

It is unusual to see a large fish receiving attention from a kissing gourami, for the latter usually kiss only their own kind. In the United States they are generally pink; this one is of the wild type, with many dark stripes on a green body.

common in the United States is the pink variety, which appears to be an albino except for the center of the eye, which is black.

Kissing gouramis belong to the labyrinth fishes, to which the Siamese fighting fish also belongs. All of the labyrinth fishes come to the surface to breathe, and all of them share a rather peculiar breeding habit, in which the male wraps himself around the female while the female expels her eggs. Most labyrinths build floating nests for their eggs, but kissing gouramis produce floating eggs that just drift away with the current. This haphazard lack of care for the eggs is compensated for by producing a large number of eggs—as many as two thousand.

Whether they kiss out of affection or for some less romantic reason, kissing gouramis are great fun to keep.

30 »• *The Lionfish*

ONCE the author saw a sign on an aquarium in a pet store that read, "Lionfish, $300.00." Inside was a twelve-inch orange, black, and white striped fish with huge plumelike fins. It was a magnificent creature, well worth the price to anyone who could afford to spend that much money for a pet. In his classic book, *Exotic Aquarium Fishes*, William T. Innes describes the lionfish (*Pterois volitans*) as "the fanciest fish alive." It may well be.

The lionfish is a South Pacific representative of a rather large and widely distributed saltwater family, the scorpion fishes. Many kinds are found along both coasts of the United States. Some of the scorpion fishes are extremely venomous; hence the origin of their common name. All of them bear some resemblance to the fine lionfish pictured here.

Many another fish and more than a few humans have lived to regret an encounter with a lionfish. Inside each of the feathery fins there is a long, sharp spine. At the base of the spine is a sack of venom. A hollow groove connects the sack with the tip of the spine. When one of the fins is touched, it causes a painful wound that can make a person very sick. An arm or leg that has been punctured by a lionfish's spines may be partially paralyzed for some time.

The lionfish appears to be fully aware of its potentialities. In

The deceptive lionfish is one of the most beautifully decorated fishes in the world. Who would guess that hidden inside those flowing plumes are poisonous spines?

an aquarium it swims about deliberately and with great boldness. When threatened, it backs into a corner and waves its fins menacingly. In the aquarium, lionfish sometimes become so tame that they will take food from their owner's fingers.

In the waters around the islands of Hawaii is a dwarf lionfish, *Dendrochirus barberi,* which is brought to the mainland occasionally, but not so often as it deserves to be. *Dendrochirus* grows to only about three inches, and it does quite well in a small saltwater aquarium. Its fins are smaller than the lionfish's, and its colors are more subdued, but it is a handsome animal nonetheless.

Both the lionfish and its miniature cousin should be kept alone in an aquarium, because they have very large mouths. They will eat fishes nearly as large as themselves.

31 »• *The Stickleback*

THE three-spined stickleback, *Gasterosteus aculeatus*, is probably the most thoroughly studied fish in the world. For years it has been the subject of intensive experiments by ethologists (biologists who study how and why animals act or behave the way they do), who have looked into virtually every aspect of the private life of this little fish. It has also been used in several other kinds of biological studies.

These are aquarium fishes that can be obtained for nothing, because a number of species are widely distributed throughout the temperate zones of the world. Anyone who lives near either coast of the United States can collect them from streams, but before doing this it is necessary to first check with the local conservation department to be sure this will not break the law. The most common species is the above-mentioned three-spined stickleback, which is found in salt, brackish, and fresh waters along both the Atlantic and Pacific coasts. It is easily identified, because it has three prominent spines sticking up in front of its dorsal fin.

Since all of the sticklebacks have similar habits, we will refer to the fascinating behavior of the three-spined stickleback. The others differ only in certain details. When the male fish is in

Because of their interesting breeding and defensive behavior, stickle-backs have been widely studied by biologists.

breeding condition, he develops a bright red coloring along his abdomen. He digs a small depression in the bottom sand and then constructs a nest from sticks and pieces of plants in the depression. He pushes sand partially over the nest to keep it anchored to the bottom. He then locates a likely female and dances around her until she is drawn near the nest. The female pushes her way into the nest, lays her eggs, and then swims out the other side. The male follows immediately and fertilizes the eggs. Once the eggs are in the nest, the male's affection turns to aggression. He viciously drives her away. If other females are nearby, the male may entice them to lay their eggs in the nest before he settles down to being a prospective father.

Father stickleback assumes a position near the nest and guards it with great courage from intruders. Occasionally, he puffs or draws water through the nest to insure the presence of fresh well-aerated water about the developing embryos. Within a few days the nest becomes a shambles, but by this time the babies have hatched. The father continues to protect his young for a time, but finally they are left to survive on their own.

Experiments have shown that vision is important in the behavior of sticklebacks. If an artificial model of a female stickleback with an enlarged abdomen (indicating the presence of eggs) is placed in front of a breeding male, he will dance in front of the model and attempt to coax it into his nest just as if it were a real female. If a model without a swollen abdomen is placed before him, the male ignores it or tries to drive it away. The red coloring of the male has been found to be important as well, for breeding, since it helps to excite the female. The red coloring is also a warning to the breeding male. If another red-bellied male comes into his territory, the father drives it away viciously. In the laboratory, red-bellied models have been placed before male sticklebacks. The male immediately attacks the model, regardless of how little the model is shaped like a fish. It is the red coloring that arouses the fish's anger.

It is not difficult to induce sticklebacks to go through their colorful breeding behavior in an aquarium.

32 »• *Flounders or Flatfishes*

MANY kinds of flatfishes are important as food for man. Most people know from firsthand experience that the huge halibuts and the much smaller flounders are delicious to eat. Very small flounders also make interesting aquarium pets.

Flatfishes are a fairly large group, with four families and about six hundred species. All of them do quite well in life despite what at first glance appears to be a severe handicap: they swim on their sides rather than upright, as other fishes do. Swimming is accomplished by a peculiar undulation of the entire

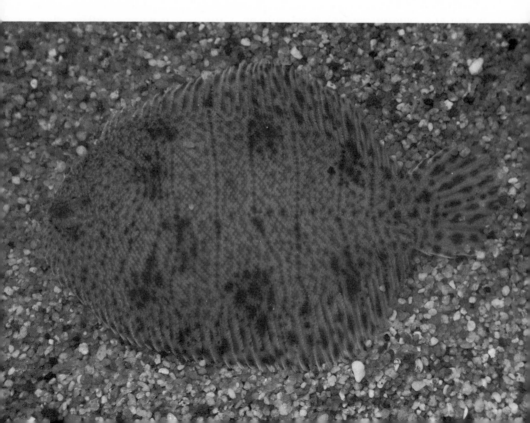

body and the fins. Typically, the flatfishes rest on the bottom or bury themselves in the bottom with only their eyes showing.

The underside of most flatfishes is white or pinkish. The top side is of some color that blends in well with the bottom. Both eyes are on the top side. Some flounders have the ability to change their coloring to match the bottom. If the bottom is composed of dark and light pebbles, these flatfishes change their markings to dark and light spots, closely imitating the bottom. If the bottom is plain tan sand, the same fish can alter its coloring to a similar shade.

In the photograph at left, a flounder has adopted the appearance of the bottom gravel so effectively that it is difficult to see. Against a white background (right), the same fish is conspicuous. If it were left on a white surface, the flounder would soon become so pale that it would again blend into the background.

The color-changing ability of some flounders has been studied by scientists in laboratories. When placed on a bottom of black-and-white checkerboard squares, some flatfishes assume a checkerboard pattern for themselves! Scientists have proven that flounders look at the bottom to determine how they should alter their coloring. When their eyes are covered, they are unable to blend in with their surroundings.

Perhaps the most remarkable peculiarity of flatfishes is *how* both eyes get to be on one side. When they are first born, baby flatfishes swim upright in normal fish fashion, and one eye is on each side. Then, while the fish is still very young, one eye begins to "migrate" to the other side. (What actually happens is that one side of the head grows faster than the other, distorting the head until both eyes are on the same side.) At the same time, the young fish begins to lean toward one side, continuing until the side that has lost its eye comes to rest on the bottom. For the rest of its life, the flounder is truly a *flat* fish.

Most flatfishes live in salt water, but some of them occasionally swim into fresh water, and a few kinds spend their entire lives in fresh water. For example, some little flounders can be found in streams of northern Peru's Amazon country—more than two thousand miles from the nearest salt water. While little is known about the habits of the Amazonian flatfishes, it seems safe to assume that they spend all of their lives in fresh water. It does seem most unlikely that any saltwater species would travel more than two thousand miles from the ocean to spawn. Of course, this assumption cannot be accepted as fact until scientific studies have proven that these flatfishes live out their complete life cycle in fresh water.

Amazonian flounders are occasionally imported for aquarists, but most of the "freshwater" flounders sold in pet shops are actually a common Atlantic species, *Trinectes maculatus,* whose young in the spring and summer are found in large numbers in brackish waters along the Gulf Coast. They do quite well in entirely fresh water.

Both eyes are positioned on the upper side of the flatfish, a change which occurs at a very early stage in the fish's life.

Flounders make interesting pets in the home aquarium, where they entertain their owner with their peculiar swimming motion. Frequently they rest on the glass sides of the aquarium, where their seldom-seen undersides may be observed.

33 »• *The Puffer*

SHORE fishermen along the Atlantic Coast of the United States often despise the puffer or blowfish. It picks the bait from their hooks, and it becomes hooked itself before other larger and more desirable fishes can be caught. Sometimes in the warmer months and in some bays and inlets the puffer is so plentiful that it is practically impossible to catch anything else.

Anyone who has ever caught one on a line knows how the puffer gets its common name. As soon as it is pulled from the water, the puffer takes great gulps of air into its mouth and inflates its abdomen until it is virtually a round ball with a head and a tail.

The puffer's ability to inflate itself is a means of defense. It can fill up with either air or water. By a special quirk of anatomy, the air or water is passed directly into the area under its skin. When threatened by a larger fish, the puffer gulps in water or air until it is too much of a mouthful to be eaten. When the danger is passed, the comical fish quickly expels the air or water and goes on about its business.

Many species of puffers are distributed throughout the warmer waters of the world. A few kinds are found in fresh water. These are the ones that occasionally find their way into home aquariums. They make most interesting pets. Several kinds are spotted. Others have solid dark colors. All of them have several characteristics in common, in addition to the ability to inflate. They roll their eyes in their heads—independently of each other if they wish. Transparent pectoral fins are kept constantly in motion, and they all have a peculiar stiff-bodied way of swimming: only the rear third of the fish bends. Because of a covering of tiny bristles, puffers have more of a lizard feel than a fish feel when they are touched, for they are not slippery. Two very powerful incisor teeth in the top jaw and two in the bottom jaw give the puffer the ability to give a painful bite, but it ordinarily uses its teeth for cracking open shellfish and crabs.

The flesh of many kinds of puffer has long been regarded as poisonous, but it is now known that only the liver, the reproductive organs, the intestines, and the skin of most "poisonous" spe-

This little puffer is frequently seen in freshwater aquariums. In the second photograph the same fish is partially inflated.

cies contain a toxic substance called tetrodotoxin. A few species are known to contain some tetrodotoxin in their muscles, but if puffers are carefully skinned and eviscerated, most kinds are safe to eat. Indeed, in some places even the more hazardous kinds are so highly regarded as food that people are willing to risk sickness by eating them. It is reported that in 1957, 176 Japanese people fell sick or died from eating puffers. Nevertheless, the puffers found along the Atlantic coast of North America make delicious eating and at times are plentiful in the markets. With the head and tough skin removed, Atlantic puffers fry into tasty, nearly boneless morsels, in shape not unlike the drumstick of a chicken.

In an aquarium, puffers are just as ravenous eaters as they are out in the wild. To be kept in good health, they must have frequent feedings of live fishes, pieces of fish, worms, snails, or

A rare freshwater puffer from Africa.

ground meat. Puffers have not been bred in captivity, but it is known that the common Atlantic species lays about 200,000 eggs.

There is a strong temptation to be constantly taking pet puffers from the water to make them inflate. Held in the palm of one hand and tickled on the belly by a finger, the puffer is usually willing to perform, but the temptation should be resisted, since puffers are as uncomfortable out of water as any other fishes. Too much tickling can result in a dead pet.

34 »• *The Sargassum Fish*

AWAY from its home, the sargassum fish, *Histrio*, is as conspicuous as an American flag fluttering in a summer sky, but at home, it blends in so well with its surroundings that smaller fishes frequently make the fatal mistake of nibbling on its head.

The sargassum fish belongs to a group called angler fishes because they all have a means of "angling" for other fishes. In all of the anglers, the first rays of the dorsal fin are modified into "fishing poles," with which the fish lures unwary prey toward its mouth. In some species the "fishing pole" is tipped with an attractive "berry." In others, including the sargassum fish, the pole is covered with fleshy appendages that *look* as though they might be good eating.

With its marbled pattern of brown, gold, and white markings, *Histrio* would be a very pretty fish if it were not so grotesquely shaped. It is a hardy and most interesting aquarium fish if one has a supply of small live fishes to feed it.

Vast areas of the Central Atlantic Ocean's warmer waters are covered with a kind of floating seaweed called *Sargassum*. One huge area east of the Bahama Islands is called the Sargasso Sea. The three-inch sargassum fish lives among the *Sargassum* seaweed. This explains how it gets its name. The little fish may live out its entire life among the seaweeds without ever coming within several hundred miles of land.

In its seaweed setting, the sargassum fish is beautifully camouflaged, since *Sargassum* weed is colored just like the fish. (Or, more accurately, the fish is colored like the seaweed.)

In its natural home among floating seaweed, the sargassum fish is invisible.

The sargassum fish remains motionless among the seaweed for long periods of time. When it does move, it is more likely to walk than swim, for its large pectoral fins are well suited to climbing among the plants. About the fish's head and mouth are many fleshy extensions. When another fish moves up to nibble on these fleshy extensions, the sargassum fish opens its huge mouth and sucks its victim in with a lightning-fast motion. It is capable of eating a fish nearly as large as itself. When it has eaten a large fish, the sargassum fish's stomach looks as though it will burst.

35 »• *Lungfishes*

Two hundred million and more years ago the waters of the earth were teeming with fishes that actually looked more like legless lizards than fishes. Their tubelike bodies were covered with coarse scales, and at the hind end there was scarcely more than a suggestion of a tail fin. The paired ventral fins and pectoral fins were heavily muscled, with more the appearance of shriveled legs than true fins. But most remarkable of all, these ancient fishes had primitive lungs, which enabled them to breathe air. They also had well-developed gills, which they could use. Evolutionists regard these primitive air breathers as possible forerunners of higher animals.

Of the countless millions of lungfishes that lived so many eons ago, only a very small remnant remains to the present time, but this remnant is fully as interesting as its ancestors of long ago.

Lungfishes today are found in a few places in Australia, Africa, and South America. They live in areas that undergo severe drought conditions during certain times of the year. As the drought progresses, the ponds gradually dry up until only the mud on the bottom remains moist. Other fishes would die at this point, but not the lungfish. It burrows into the moist mud and keeps on burrowing as long as the moisture lasts. Finally even most of this moisture is gone, and the lungfish must do something drastic or perish. It goes into a period of sleep called estivation. Curling itself into a ball, it secretes a layer of mucus, which, in the African kinds, dries like leather. The slime remains moist in the South American species. Only the mouth remains protruding through the fish's "cocoon." Rate of breathing drops from fifteen times per minute to once every several hours. Heartbeat drops to about two times per minute.

All living things need nourishment and produce waste products, regardless of how inactive they are. During estivation, lungfishes "feed" on their own body tissues, which are slowly absorbed. By the time its forced sleep comes to an end, a lungfish is a sorry, skinny sight. Instead of eliminating its waste products, as it ordinarily would do, the lungfish retains them for the whole period of estivation. They build up to a concentration that would kill any other animal. Humans, for example, are likely to die if waste in the bloodstream rises to ten parts per million. The lungfish's wastes may build up to as high as 20,000 parts per million, and still the fish lives on.

When the rainy season starts, and the ponds begin to fill with water again, the lungfish becomes active immediately. Waste products are eliminated, and the fish eats everything in sight until it restores its emaciated body to normal size and weight.

As soon as the lungfishes regain their strength, they make plans to reproduce, for they seem to know instinctively that their young must be born and reared to a good size before the next dry period begins. The African and South American lungfishes are attentive parents. They dig a burrow in a mud bank or on the bottom of the pond. In this the eggs are laid and fertilized. The male guards the burrow and periodically swishes his tail over the eggs, apparently to keep the water moving over his young. Any intruder is driven away by a savage attack.

An Australian lungfish. All lungfishes have primitive lungs in addition to gills. During the dry season lungfishes burrow in the mud, where they survive until the next rainy season. Without their lungs they would quickly die under such conditions.

When the babies hatch, they remain in or near the burrow for some time. In their immature stage, lungfishes reveal another link to higher animals, because they at first have four sets of feathery gill filaments extending from the sides of their heads.

Immature amphibians of many kinds also have such filaments.

Australian lungfishes differ from their African and South American cousins in two important ways. They are poor parents. The eggs are merely scattered among plants and then left to the mercy of their surroundings. The young of the Australian lungfish do not possess gill filaments.

Small brown-colored lungfishes are occasionally sold to aquarists (they grow to over five feet), and they make interesting pets, even though the African lungfish is vicious to other fishes. The South American lungfish is reasonably peaceful.

Feeding pet lungfish is not difficult, for they readily eat pieces of meat and fish. At feeding time, lungfishes are a laughable sight, because they have such poor vision. They cock their heads in a most unfishlike manner and then suddenly lunge at the food. As often as not they miss and must make another try.

No public aquarium is complete without at least one large lungfish.

Scientific Names of Fishes

Most laymen shy away from the long Latin and Greek names given to living things by biologists, but they do serve a very valuable purpose. Common names vary from place to place and from country to country, but scientific names do not. For instance, whether he speaks English, German, French, or some other language, the biologist knows that *Anguilla* refers to the eels of the Atlantic coasts of America and Europe. Scientific names form a universal language for biologists. Without them it would be impossible to keep track of the millions of kinds of living things in this world. Following is a list of the common and scientific names of fishes mentioned in this book.

COMMON NAME	SCIENTIFIC NAME
blind cave tetra	*Anoptichthys jordani*
hatchet fishes	*Gasteropelecus levis*
	Carnegiella marthae
piranha	*Serrasalmus* (several species)
copeina	*Copeina arnoldi*
electric eel	*Electrophorus electricus*
electric catfish	*Malapterurus electricus*
goldfish	*Carassius auratus*
European bitterling	*Rhodeus sericeus*
upside-down catfish	*Synodontis nigriventris*
common eel (European)	*Anguilla anguilla*
common eel (American)	*Anguilla bostoniensis*
halfbeak	*Dermogenys pusillus*

COMMON NAME	SCIENTIFIC NAME
desert pupfish	*Cyprinodon nevadensis*
Argentine pearl fish	*Cynolebias nigripinnis* and *Cynolebias bellottii*
African annual fish	*Nothobranchius guentheri*
mosquito fish	*Heterandria formosa*
guppy	*Lebistes reticulatus* or *Poecilia reticulata*
wagtail platy	*Xiphophorus maculatus*
four-eyed fish	*Anableps anableps*
Atlantic sea horse	*Hippocampus erectus*
Pacific sea horse	*Hippocampus kuda*
dwarf sea horse	*Hippocampus zosterae*
banded chaetodon	*Mesogonistius chaetodon*
archer fish	*Toxotes jaculator*
badis	*Badis badis*
Amazon leaf fish	*Monocirrhus polyacanthus*
African mouthbreeder	*Tilapia mossambica*
Egyptian mouthbreeder	*Haplochromis multicolor*
angelfish	*Pterophyllum scalare*
discus fish	*Symphysodon discus*
marine clownfish	*Amphiprion percula*
mudskipper	*Periophthalmus barbarus*
climbing perch	*Anabas testudineus*
Siamese fighting fish	*Betta splendens*
kissing gourami	*Helostoma temmincki*
lionfish	*Pterois volitans*
dwarf lionfish	*Dendrochirus barberi*
stickleback	*Gasterosteus aculeatus*
freshwater flounder	*Trinectes maculatus* and others
freshwater puffer	*Tetraodon fluviatilis* and others
Sargassum fish	*Histrio histrio*
Australian lungfish	*Neoceratodus forsteri*
African lungfish	*Protopterus annectens*
South American lungfish	*Lepidosiren paradoxa*

Some Helpful Books and Magazines for People Interested in Fishes

Axelrod, H. R. and Schultz, L. P. (1955). *Handbook of Tropical Aquarium Fishes*. New York: McGraw-Hill.

Axelrod, H. R. and Vorderwinkler, W. (1962). *Encyclopedia of Tropical Fishes*. Jersey City, N.J.: T.F.H. Publications.

Eddy, Samuel (1957). *How to Know the Freshwater Fishes*. Dubuque, Iowa: W. C. Brown Co. An excellent guide to North American fishes.

Herald, Earl S. (1961). *Living Fishes of the World*. Garden City, N.Y.: Doubleday & Co., Inc.

Hubbs, C. L. and Lagler, C. F. (1958). *Fishes of the Great Lakes Region*. Bloomfield Hills, Mich.: Cranbrook Institute of Science.

Innes, William T. (1967). *Exotic Aquarium Fishes,* 19th ed. rev. Maywood, N.J.: Aquariums, Inc. The aquarist's "Bible." Probably the most helpful book in this list. Older editions are also worth buying.

Schultz, L. C. and Stern, E. M. (1948). *The Ways of Fishes*. Princeton, N.J.: Van Nostrand Co.

Simkatis, Helen. (1958). *Salt-Water Fishes for the Home Aquarium*. Philadelphia: J. B. Lippincott Co.

The Aquarium. Monthly. Published by Aquariums, Inc., Maywood, N.J.

Tropical Fish Hobbyist. Monthly. Published by T.F.H. Publications, 245 Cornelison Ave., Jersey City, N.J. 07302

Definitions of Some Words Used in This Book

adaptation—a change to fit some special use.

aggression—the act of attacking or fighting.

anatomy—the parts of animals or plants.

appendage—a thing attached to something else. A tail is an appendage.

biologist—a scientist who studies living things.

brackish—a mixture of fresh and salt water, usually where a river empties into the sea.

camouflage—special coloring, markings, or structures that permit an animal to blend into its surroundings.

crustaceans—a large group of aquatic and marine animals that have hard shells. A crab is a crustacean. Small crustaceans are valuable food for many fishes.

drought—a long period without rain.

embryo—an unborn or unhatched living thing, usually associated with an egg.

estivation—a condition of sleep or rest that some animals go into during hot weather.

exotic—from a faraway place.

fertilize—to make an egg so that it will develop into an embryo. A female's eggs are fertilized by sperms from a male fish.

fry—a newborn fish.

fungus—a kind of primitive plant. Many microscopic fungi (plural for fungus) cause diseases in animals.

gelatinous—like jelly.

genes—microscopic parts of sperms and eggs that pass a plant's or animal's characteristics on to the next generation.

genetics—the branch of biology that studies how characteristics are passed from generation to generation.

gill—the organ through which a fish breathes. Fishes have gills; higher animals have lungs.

gonopodium—a specially developed anal fin of certain male fishes. The male fish uses his gonopodium to place sperms inside the female.

ichthyologist—a biologist who studies fishes.

impulse—a signal sent out by light, electricity, sound, or some other means.

incubate—to care for eggs in some way until they hatch.

instinct—behavior that appears to be inherited.

leptocephali—the young of eels before they take on the appearance typical of eels.

mucus—the slimy covering of fishes and other animals.

nutritious—having great value as food.

offspring—the young of living things.

ovipositor—a tube developed by the females of certain animals at breeding time. It is used for depositing eggs.

pigment—a substance that gives color to living things. Some fish colors are caused by pigments.

retina—the sensitive lining on the back of the eye. It is the part of the eye that "sees," similar in function to the film in a camera.

spawn—to lay eggs. Also, a group of eggs is sometimes called a "spawn."

species—a distinct kind of plant or animal.

specimen—a sample or example of something.

sperm—the microscopic cell of a male that fertilizes the egg of a female.

spherical—shaped like a ball.

stagnant—foul from standing still for a long time.

suffocate—to die from lack of air.

symbiosis—a condition in which two different living things live together, each receiving some benefit from the other.

tentacles—long, flexible growths usually near the head or mouth of certain animals. Used to grasp food, they often possess stingers.

tidal—the area near the mouth of a river where the height of the river rises and lowers with the tides of the ocean.

toxic—poisonous.

venom—the poison produced by certain animals.

venomous—having the ability to produce poison.

voracious—greedy in eating; having a great appetite.

Index